STRANGER AT KILLKNOCK

Also *by* LEONARD WIBBERLEY

The Hands of Cormac Joyce

The Quest of Excalibur

Beware of the Mouse

Take Me to Your President

McGillicuddy McGotham

The Mouse That Roared

Mrs. Searwood's Secret Weapon

NONFICTION

The Trouble with the Irish

The Coming of the Green

No Garlic in the Soup

The Land That Isn't There

Yesterday's Land

JUVENILES (Fiction)

Peter Treegate's War

Kevin O'Connor and the Light Brigade

The Wound of Peter Wayne

John Treegate's Musket

Sea Captain from Salem

Deadmen's Cave

JUVENILES (Nonfiction)

Wes Powell—Conqueror of the Colorado

The Life of Winston Churchill

John Barry—Father of the Navy

The Epics of Everest

Leonard Wibberley

STRANGER
AT KILLKNOCK

G. P. Putnam's Sons
New York

Library of Congress Catalog

Card Number: 61-8352

MANUFACTURED IN THE UNITED STATES OF AMERICA

VAN REES PRESS • NEW YORK

For Julian Brodetsky

STRANGER AT KILLKNOCK

Chapter One

THE village was called Killknock (that being the English spelling) but the name translated from the Irish meant the Church on the Mountain. A mountain was indeed its principal feature—a huge head and shoulders of a mountain that rose behind the village and seemed to be peering at it and debating whether the village should be allowed to continue or should be obliterated by the power that lay in the mountain.

The mountain was powerful indeed. Everybody in the village knew that.

Its base was in the boglands around, but the mountain rose steadily above these and on its gaunt flanks rare

9

plants grew, which were in themselves some token of the power of the mountain.

These plants grew nowhere else in Ireland nor in Europe for that matter. They were exclusive to the mountain whose name was Knockmor—the Great Mountain. It had another name—Knockmaan; but this was a secret name which wasn't used any more. It was secret because it was forbidden and had been forbidden for about sixteen hundred years, for Knockmaan (again translated into the English) meant the Mountain of Mananaan, or by extension the Throne of Mananaan.

And Mananaan was the old pagan god of the sea. Christianity could not tolerate such a name.

Still, there were some strange things about the mountain other than the rare plants which it supported. There was for instance a shallow lake at its foot, on the other side from the village. It was called the Lake of the Stones. Every first of November at midnight the big upright stones on the peak of the mountain lumbered down the side, wobbling and weaving, to take a long drink in the Lake of the Stones. Then they went back to the peak again. Anyone who saw them in this performance would be turned into a boulder. That was the story. It was such a story as is not believed in daytime, and yet is not disbelieved at nighttime. There are many such stories in Ireland, which is a land of stories.

There were not more than two hundred people in

the village, all of them Catholics except the district
medical officer who was a Protestant, and from the Six
Counties. He was a small and thickset man with a red
face and a red nose and a sharp tongue. His hair was
sparse and he was reckoned young, being in his mid-
forties. His disposition was not improved by the suspi-
cion that everybody in the village had instructions from
the parish priest, Father Michael Dimmock, to pray for
his conversion to Roman Catholicism. It is a hard thing
for a man to have a whole village praying for his
conversion to a faith against which his ancestors had
fought for several centuries. It made Dr. McEwan more
short-tempered than he was by nature and when the
Mass bell rang at six o'clock on a Sunday morning, he
would pull the covers over his head to cut off or at
least muffle the sound, as if the very chimes might waft
him, against his will, into the place of worship of the
papists.

"They're a simple and benighted people," he once
said of the villagers, "full of superstitions about holy
water, scapulars, retreats, pilgrimages, pagan gods and
Guinness." But it was the simplicity of the villagers that
had brought him from Belfast to practice among them.
He didn't want the villagers to change. He liked the
people the way they were, and when he needed conversation on topics other than weather, sheep, fish and
rheumatism he could always turn to Father Dimmock,
though, of course, he wouldn't visit the priest's house

lest the joyous rumor that he was "seeking instruction" spread through Killknock. The priest had to come to him, making it plain, Dr. McEwan hoped, that the visit was social and not theological.

Killknock faced the Atlantic. It was a fishing village and had a little harbor in which the villagers kept their curraghs and pucans when they were not fishing. The harbor mole had been built after the Famine in 1845 and had well withstood the Atlantic gales for over a century. The rise of tide was seventeen feet, though a spring tide would rise twenty-four feet. It follows that the village was on a hill—indeed on a flank of Knockmor, the mountain. So was the church. It was higher up the flank and dominated the whole village. But the mountain itself, the old mountain of the sea god Mananaan, overlooked them all.

When the tide was low, the harbor had but a foot or two of water at its deepest part, so that boats could not get in and out at low tide. They rolled over on their sides, or the heavier ones settled on cradles which were lashed to the bottom of the boat and taken off when the pucan was to put to sea.

The receding tide exposed the stout ribs of a hooker which had been allowed to rot in the harbor during the first World War. In the summer evenings the men would gather at the sea wall overlooking the harbor and at low tide their talk would turn to the old hooker.

She had been a great ship in her day. She was not

just a fishing vessel but could carry cargo, and her chief employment had been carrying turf down to Galway, thirty-five miles down the coast. Once, however, she had made a voyage to America. Old Tom Joyce had been on her, and he liked to talk about that voyage.

"There was myself and Pateen King and Sean O'-Reilly and Patrick Conneeley," he would say. "We were out beyond Inishlacken—about sixty mile—well past the Hags, and the wind was from Gaul. Sean started talking about his brother that was in Boston and how he would like to see him.

" 'We could make it in ten days,' said Pateen. 'And we've food for two weeks.' And between talking backwards and forwards about it and the turf not yet ready to be shipped to Galway and wouldn't be for a month with the sun waiting on the wind, and fish scarce anyway, why we decided we'd time and to spare to go to Boston.

"And so we went."

They didn't make Boston however, but Halifax, Nova Scotia, and had then run down the coast to Boston only to find that Sean O'Reilly's brother had gone to Philadelphia. So they came back, ten weeks later, by which time the turf was ready for shipment and they were the heroes of Connemara.

Now the hooker that made the voyage was sunk in the bottom of the harbor and the only survivor was old Tom Joyce who was somewhere in his sixties.

He was a big man, white-haired and rough-featured. His nose seemed to be getting a little longer with age, but there was nothing feeble about him.

He pulled a good oar in a curragh, set his own lobster pots, put out his own nets and drank two big glasses of Guinness each evening at Feeney's saloon. He was reckoned the most knowledgeable fisherman in the village and it was in his curragh that the priest went over to the island—Inishlacken—whenever necessary to visit the sick. Tom would get him there whatever the weather, for he and the Atlantic had half a century of acquaintance.

He knew the set of the currents and the force of them and how they changed their paths from week to week. He knew where best to catch pollack and conger eels and where the best beds of scallops were to be found and where lobsters were at any particular month.

He could tell from the size and frequency of the waves what kind of weather there was far out in the ocean and he could tell when rain was coming, or wind, or sudden sea mist. Most of the villagers were fishermen but Tom Joyce was something different. He was a seaman, as some people are land-men. The priest, Father Dimmock, sometimes thought that the sea had permeated Tom Joyce's body and told him things which others could not hear. It was a tide of sea water, rather than blood, that ran in his veins. Or maybe it was that Mananaan had Tom Joyce specially in his charge.

Father Dimmock of course did not believe in Mananaan any more than he did in the giants which populated fairy stories. But he often wondered whether Tom Joyce was really praying to Saint Brendan, the patron of Irish fishermen, when he had a rough passage from Killknock to the island, and if so, why he kept his eyes on the mountain behind the village while the wind whistled around them and the seas hissed and foamed about the curragh, and the appalling loneliness and power of the ocean were about them.

He once asked Old Tom why he kept his eyes constantly on the mountain when they were at sea in troubled weather and he had replied, "It is to keep us safe, Father." The reply was enigmatic. An oarsman kept a point of land in view to steer his course and the mountain was a good landmark. But Father Dimmock wondered whether there was not another meaning in the answer—a meaning that referred in a veiled and secret way to Mananaan, the sea god. In any case there was a feeling in the village that between Tom and the sea there was a pact; a secret understanding, as if the two were allies, the one of the other. This belief stemmed from the time of the White Storm, which was ten years before.

It had been called the White Storm because preceding it, for three days, the sky has been covered with cloud of a peculiar luminosity. It had been white cloud like a snow field up in the sky. But the light being from overhead and almost equally from all sides, no man or tree or animal in Killknock had for three days cast a discernible shadow upon the earth. That had filled the villagers with fear because the shadow of a man was a mark of his mortal life. When the devil appeared, you could tell him by the fact that he had no shadow. This was true also of banshees, for neither the devil nor the banshee had a mortal life. When, therefore, the strange light of the sky had been such that no one in the village could see his shadow, the villagers had been terrified, believing that they were all marked for death.

They had not fled immediately but had stayed hoping the storm would break elsewhere. They went on with their tasks and the men had even gone out in their curraghs to fish, for the sea did not rise with the strange light, nor was there any great quantity of wind.

When the storm struck there were eight curraghs fishing in the Atlantic. Tom Joyce was in one of them and had a boy with him. Tom was the sole survivor of the little curragh fleet, for he had ridden out the storm, the whole thirty-six hours of it, keeping awake all the time, bailing his curragh, keeping her head on to the terrible waves with the oars.

For thirty-six hours he had done this and then he had brought the curragh back. But the boy was not with him. He had been drowned. The villagers had left finally when the storm struck, and when they came back it was to find Tom Joyce alone in the village. He would not tell them anything except that the boy who was with him was drowned. The bodies of some of the other men drowned in the storm were found. Some were washed ashore and one was brought up in a net a week later. His widow recognized him by the jersey she had knit for him, for his face was gone. But the body of the boy was not found. Still that was not so strange, the tide being what it was and the currents fast flowing off the coast. The boy's body had been taken far out to sea, without a doubt, and the fish had eaten it. But it was after this that the people of Killknock began to feel that there was something special between Tom Joyce and the sea; a pact or an understanding by which the sea would spare Tom Joyce and he would never be drowned in it.

They said of him, "He'll never drown," and gave a little knowing laugh afterwards but would explain themselves no further, not even to Father Dimmock, which annoyed the priest who was not long from the college at Maynooth and dubious about some of the superstitions of his parishioners.

Inishlacken, the island six miles off the coast, although it formed a part of the parish, was by no means a part of the village. The islanders made their curraghs in a different way from the men of Killknock. They did not use as many laths or withies for the framework over which the tarred canvas was stretched, for one thing. And they built the bows higher. They made their fishing pots in a different manner also. These differences made for a foreignness between the two groups.

Also it was held in Killknock that the men of Inish-lacken were not to be trusted. They were clannish and would gang up on a man from Killknock if they could, though they pretended friendliness.

There were six families on Inishlacken which was an island not more than a mile at its longest and three quarters of a mile at its widest. They had no harbor so the men carried their boats up to their houses and put them under the lee side of the house. They didn't buy much from the village shops, which was another reason for not liking them, and the Irish they spoke was full of words that had little currency in Killknock. So the two —the men of Killknock and the men of Inishlacken— were two sects within the parish, tolerating one another but with animosities likely to flare up at any moment. The connecting link between the two was the priest, Father Dimmock, and the doctor, McEwan.

Father Dimmock's parish extended for many miles inland. The circuit of it was twenty-seven miles and it took in wild boglands and wilder mountains beyond Knockmor on which there were one or two small farms. In Killknock English was spoken but in the remoter areas of the parish, the people spoke Irish so the priest had to be bilingual. Dr. McEwan, however, had only one language, English. He knew some Irish but he refused to use it. He was a loyal subject of the British crown and he would speak no other tongue.

Although the villagers were Christians and Catholics they hesitated to climb The Great Mountain and they were afraid to go out on the night that the stones came down to the Lake of Stones for their yearly drink. This greatly angered the priest, who was comparatively new to the parish, and he had spoken to the bishop about it and suggested that Holy Mass might be celebrated on top of the mountain some Easter morning to take away the baleful influence it had upon the minds of the villagers. But the bishop merely chuckled and told him to forget about the mountain and concentrate on teaching the people of his parish.

"They have always had the mountain," he said. "You cannot get rid of it with one Mass."

With that the priest had to be content.

Chapter Two

THE day the stranger came to the village, Caitlin the Other House was driving an ass with two baskets of turf slung across its back down the bog road toward Killknock. The ass belonged to Sean Rincey the cobbler and he had not wanted to lend it to Caitlin the Other House, for it was the only donkey he had and a pretty jenny ass. It was young and healthy, white on the undersides and a pale gray on its back and the True Cross marked on it down the spine and over the shoulders to show that it was on an ass that Christ had ridden into Jerusalem before his crucifixion. No, he had not wanted to lend the beast to Caitlin the Other House but he dared not refuse her.

If he had not lent it to her the ass would have been sick the next day and she herself was the only one in the village who could physic it. So Caitlin the Other House was walking behind the ass on the bog road, watching the way it put its little hoofs so delicately one before the other and enjoying the warmth of the sun on her thin shoulders through her shawl and thinking she would be able to get some carrigeen—the green edible seaweed— off the rocks that very evening, when she saw the stranger sitting by the foot of a stack of turf that had been put by the roadside to be taken away by Pat Conneeley's lorry in a day or two.

She had been looking at the stack of turf as she came down the road thinking she might stop there a bit and rest her feet, and had seen no one by it. And suddenly there was a man by the foot of it and not a man from the village because he had on the kind of clothes the idle people wore that walked or drove around Ireland in the summer.

Well, she said to herself, he wasn't there before but he's here now and there's a mystery to him and the first part of the mystery is how he got here at all. There isn't a bus from Galway until three in the afternoon and it's scarcely past noon. And he did not come by car, for I would have seen and heard the car. And he did not come by bicycle, for there is no bicycle by him. And he did not walk here either, for you could see a hare move a mile down the road in this pleasant weather and

I have seen nothing move since I left the bog but three sheep and a crow. But isn't it good fortune that I should be the first one in Killknock to see him and me driving the prettiest donkey in the village?

Caitlin the Other House was about sixty years of age, but a woman and unmarried. So she hitched her shawl a little to give it a better set on her shoulders and smoothed her hair which was white and long and tied in a bun on the back of her head, for a woman is as much a woman at sixty as she is at six.

"Good day to you, sir," she said when she was abreast of the stranger, and for all her sixty years and the troubles she had seen, she blushed.

The stranger got up slowly and with remarkable grace. "Good day," he said and smiled at her. It was a friendly and warm smile and Caitlin the Other House said to herself that if it had been raining she would not have got wet nor cold with a smile like that on her. The jenny ass, which had been looking at the stranger for a moment, now came slowly over to him and the stranger put out his hand and rubbed his knuckles between the ass's ears.

"Ye have a way with the beasts I see, sir," said Caitlin.

"Ah, he's a friend of mine," said the stranger. He looked the ass over and traced the markings of the cross on its back. They grew, a deep brown stripe of hair along the spine and down the forequarters, and seemed to interest him.

22

"Are all Irish donkeys marked like that?" he asked.

"They are to be sure," said Caitlin. " 'Tis because it was on a donkey that Christ Himself entered Jerusalem on Palm Sunday."

"An Irish donkey?" asked the stranger with the ghost of a teasing smile.

Holy Mother of God, I'll bet he's a Protestant, said Caitlin to herself. And me with my big mouth talking nonsense to him that was given me by the nuns in my childhood.

"Ah well," she said, "it's just a saying, do you see?"

"I was only teasing about Irish donkeys," said the stranger.

"There wasn't any Irish donkeys in them days," said Caitlin. "Indeed there wasn't any Irish for that matter, but just pagans inhabiting the whole place. But you'll probably know more about that than I do myself."

"Yes," said the stranger. He pointed to the mountain visible toward the horizon down the road.

"Tell me," he said, "is that Knockmaan?"

"Ah! We don't call it Knockmaan at all," said Caitlin. "Knockmor is what it is called."

"But the real name is Knockmaan. Isn't that right?"

"Well, it's not the name that we put on it," said Caitlin diplomatically, for she did not want to contradict a stranger and particularly such a very pleasant one. "I believe it was called Knockmaan in the old times, but now it is Knockmor."

"In the old times," repeated the stranger. "That was before the coming of Saint Patrick?"

"That is so, sir," said Caitlin. "You'll be interested in the plants on the mountain, perhaps. There's some of the strangest plants up there that you ever saw, so I'm told. There's plants that eats flies and some that eats moths and some that eats children—though that's just old talk. Still, there's a kind of a plant up there that if you stand on it, it will drain all the food out of you in a second and you'll be starving and trembling with hunger and if you don't eat that very minute you'll be dead the next one."

"Is that so?" said the stranger. "What's the name of that plant?"

"I don't know the English name for it. But the Irish name is *fearnas na-n ocras*. It means the plant of hunger."

"What does it look like?"

"There's the mystery of it," said Caitlin. "There isn't a person could tell you and sure you could not blame them, for with the fierce hunger that is on them when they step on the plant all they care about is eating whatever they can find so that they won't drop dead in a minute. Did it ever occur to you, sir, that it is only a man who has not been attacked by a tiger that can give you a good description of the beast?"

"I hadn't thought of it," said the stranger.

"Well now, 'tis true. For what kind of a description would you give if one came leaping out of the jungle straight at your throat when you weren't expecting it at all? Could you tell whether it had four legs or half a dozen, or whether the stripes on it ran lengthwise or along the body or whether indeed it was striped at all?"

"I see what you mean," said the stranger.

" 'Tis the same thing with the plant of hunger," said Caitlin. "Nobody that was a victim ever stopped long enough to look at it. And the rest of us, sure we wouldn't know it if we saw it in our stew. I suppose that you'll be going to the mountain looking for the queer plants that are on it?"

"Not especially," said the stranger. "Though I am interested in the mountain. But I have been struck by the truth of what you said about tigers."

"In what way were you struck by it, sir?"

"It applies to many things besides tigers. Enemies for instance. Many a man does not know his own enemy though others who are not involved can recognize him."

"It is a true word that you have spoken there," said Caitlin.

"And I suppose that there are many of us who if they found themselves in the presence of the devil would find him very likable and would not recognize him for what he was at all."

The Lord between me and all harm, said Caitlin to herself, is it Lucifer himself that I've met up with on the road, and set my shawl at? She crossed herself quickly, recalling that the stranger had seemingly appeared from nowhere, which was a trick the devil was very handy at. And he was handsome, without a doubt, and the devil was the handsomest being in Hell, or so she believed. She glanced quickly at the ground behind him and was greatly relieved to see that he had a shadow, for the devil has no shadow at all.

Well then, she said, he must be a Catholic for the Protestants do not believe in the devil and a bad time they'll all have of it when they come face to face with him on Judgment Day shortly after the start of the proceedings. And if he's a Catholic, there'll be no harm talking to him, though I wish he was an American for they are more amusing.

They started now, by common consent, to walk in the direction of Killknock and the jenny ass kept turning around and looking with what seemed to be affection at the stranger. The air had the soft blueness common to the west of Ireland and across the sky wandered flocks of clouds like fleeces in the heavens. They were not white altogether, but tinged with gold in parts and purple shadows in others and in places they were pulled so thin that the azure above showed through, a paler and more entrancing blue.

The two could see for miles around over the rolling boglands with the wild flax blooming on it and also a tuft or two of deep emerald furze and in the places where there was water the flat pale leaves of water lilies with their marble-cool blossoms. Along the road the wild iris grew, a deeper gold in the pale gold of the sunshine, and all this landscape changed with every minute through the play of the clouds overhead. Brightly lit areas were suddenly dark, hills lost in shadow slowly lighted up and came into being and then died away into obscurity again. A large and solitary white heron stood in a shallow pool no great distance off, his bill down on his breast while he scanned the crystal world below him for frogs or small fish, and indeed, all around, the lonely loveliness of the boglands and the appearing and disappearing hills, conjured into being by a change of sunlight, and the wide sweep of the ocean beyond was an enchantment.

Caitlin had often seen such days as this but not since her childhood had she felt as if the world belonged to her and all in it made for her wonder and pleasure. Her feet did not hurt her any more and her heart, which had been vexed by the countless little anxieties of living, did not trouble her any more. She looked at the white heron with pleasure and smiled as if the bird and they shared some special understanding and would be friends and remember each other for the rest of their lives.

"God's blessing on the day," she said. "It is a darling day; and I would not now be any other place but in Ireland, not any spot in Ireland, but here on the road in the sun and pleasant air."

"God bless the day indeed," said the stranger gently.

They did not say anything further to each other. A mood so exquisite and so fragile had settled upon them both that a word would have shattered it. And so they went along in silence, except for the pretty patter of the donkey's little feet and the whisper of the wind in the wild iris and the grasses and the quick chirping of birds made all the more delightful for the expectant silences that followed.

Caitlin the Other House lived in a cottage perhaps two hundred yards outside of Killknock. It was from this cottage that she got the name by which she was called in the village. There had been on the site a large gaunt building such as only the Irish are able to build— slab sides, gray, tiled with slate and with windows in it like the eye sockets in a skull. This house had been burned down during the troubles. The cottage had been called "the other house" and since Caitlin lived in it, so she got her name. Her real name was Feargal, but no one ever called her that.

When she got to the gate in the stone wall that ran around her cottage she called to the ass to stop and said, "I'll be leaving you now, sir. I'll be seeing you again, please God." It was more of a question than a statement.

"You will indeed," said the stranger and went off toward the village.

When she had turned the ass into the yard, Caitlin stood at the gate watching the stranger walking down the road. She watched him with tenderness and with sorrow and with love, for she felt like a young girl such was the effect he had had upon her.

"My love to you, stranger," she said quietly. "My love before you on the road that you may walk upon it. My love to you that you made the sun warm again, and the bird's song sweet, and the wind like music on a little flute in my ears."

Then she turned and walked into her house and she did not look like a woman in her sixties, but like a girl in the spring of life.

Chapter Three

THERE was no hotel in Killknock though Feeney, who kept a bar in the middle of the village convenient to the harbor, rented out a room or two on the upstairs floor to the more adventurous tourists who came to the village in the summer. There was really no call for a hotel in the village, for Killknock was a place that people only passed through.

To be sure, such people were aware when they came to it that here was a place such as they had never seen before; a primitive place belonging to a world far far different from the one in which they lived, day to day.

The grim little houses were different, all gray and all

tiled with slate and all crowded together like so many convicts in a prison yard. And the grim, bold head of the mountain was different. And the people they saw in the one street through the village seemed different—big-boned and raw of face and hand, the women always with a shawl over their shoulders and clad in dresses which were mere coverings and made no pretense at femininity, and the men in rough-knit jerseys and baggy tweed trousers, all with the appearance that they had never known the day when they were new.

So tourists, passing through Killknock, sensed the primitive atmosphere of the place and sensed the deepness of it and felt afraid and incapable of dealing with it. And so they passed on.

Of other visitors, there were usually only botanists—botanists from England and botanists from Germany and once a botanist from New Zealand. These, if they stayed at all, usually stayed with the priest or with Dr. Mc-Ewan, having letters of recommendation to one or the other. Theirs were the only two houses that provided accommodation of the kind that people from the outer world would expect. But the stranger, when he came to the village, stayed at neither of these places. Instead, he walked into Feeney's bar, which had a tiny grocery in the front—the bar being in a back room behind a rag of a curtain—and asked for a glass of Guinness.

There were four or five men in the bar at the time—Tom Joyce, standing as usual in the corner with one elbow on the plank that served as a bar, and a look to him as if he were at a ship's rail, eying the scud and gloom ahead and perhaps ready to call for a change of course—and Rincey the cobbler, small as a marmoset, stringy and quiet as a kitten. Rincey had his mouth continually pursed through the habit of keeping the nails for his cobbling in his mouth. His cheeks were sunken, their collapse accentuated by the pursing of his lips, and his skin was like old leather which has become thin and bleached by lying about in rain and sun. His eyes were a pale blue, pale almost to gray, and the only thing big about him were his hands which seemed to have been enlarged by the cutting and shaping and hammering of leather in which he had been engaged for twoscore years.

Also in the bar was Tim Conneeley. He was the son of the same Pat Conneeley who had sailed with Tom Joyce in the old hooker to America. He had carroty red hair and a noble forehead but no more of a chin than a turnip has. His jawbone just dwindled away to nothing under his small and feminine mouth. He wore a caubin of knitted wool on his head. The wool had been white when the caubin was first made, but the only washings it ever received was when it fell into the sea at one time or another. So now the caubin was grayish and had a brown stain at the top, for Tim Conneeley used it as much to keep his plug of tobacco in as to keep the top of his carroty head warm.

The men had been talking of a conger eel that Tim

had taken the previous night about eleven o'clock. It had been about ten feet long and weighed nine stone and Tim had had the devil's own time getting it into the boat and killing it once he had it there. There is only one place you can kill a conger eel and that is a spot behind its snakelike head into which you must drive your knife. With ten feet of eel writhing around in his curragh and playing hob with his gear, and the moon just risen, and the eel snapping at him and flaying around so that it was likely to stove a hole in the canvas of the curragh, Tim said he'd have thrown it out, line and all, but that the hook was new and the lead sinker on it, one of three pounds, a piece of property he was not prepared to part with.

"The eels should be the other side of the world at this time of year," said Tom Joyce. "In the Sargasso Sea is where they should be. It is a place of seaweed full of ships that have sailed into it and cannot get out, and skeletons on every one of them. It is the weed that holds them up, for their bottoms are gone long ago. And that's where the eels should be at this time of the year. It's strange you should find one here."

"Well, I found it," said Tim. "And when I got the hook out of him at last it was all bent up the way the eel chewed on it going down."

It was at this moment that the stranger gently moved aside the curtain that separated the bar from the little grocery store and stood for a moment, with the light

33

from the street behind him so that he seemed to be standing in a glow, looking at them.

Rincey the cobbler had his back to the curtain and the stranger and he did not look around, for it would not have been polite to do so. But he was curious nonetheless about who had come in, and seeking information, he looked at Tom Joyce, who, standing in the corner, would not fail to see the stranger. The look he saw on Tom Joyce's face was one between wonder and fear, as if he were seeing a man whom he believed long dead, or at least someone who had been away a long long time and had returned unexpectedly. This look lasted only a second and then Tom Joyce dropped his head and passed his hands over his eyes as if the light from the street hurt them.

"What would be your pleasure, sir?" said Feeney, darting his bald head through the door that led from his own quarters into the bar.

"Something to drink," said the stranger.

"Would a bottle of Guinness be the answer?" asked Feeney.

"A glass will serve," said the stranger indicating the big pint glass that Tom Joyce had in his hand.

Now there's a strange thing, said Rincey to himself. He doesn't talk like an Irishman and yet he knows that a draft Guinness is ten times the drink that a bottle of Guinness is. If he were an Englishman he would have asked for a bottle of Guinness and if he were an American he would have asked for a bottle of Guinness and if he were an Irishman from Dublin or Cork he would have asked for a bottle of Guinness to show he was one of the quality. But he wants a glass of Guinness and what is stranger about it is that Feeney can hear him. Many's the time, Rincey continued to himself, I've sat here with a roaring thirst and hammered on the counter hard enough to be heard on the other side of Galway and Feeney didn't hear me, for he's as deaf as an old sheep. And yet he heard this gentleman come in and Feeney knew what he was saying. It's a strange thing indeed, and stranger than Tim Conneeley catching that conger eel that should have been in the sea of weeds at the other side of the world. And then Rincey remembered the look, half of recognition and half of surprise or perhaps it was fear, that had come over Tom Joyce's face when the stranger walked in, and he concluded that the reason the stranger had come to Killknock was to find Tom Joyce. He had some business with him.

When Feeney had poured the stranger his Guinness, with the men watching him, with fondness and appreciation, take the creamy half off it with a wooden paddle, there was a little silence in the bar. They felt shy. Strangers were rarely among them. Nobody wanted to be the first to speak in his presence, and yet something must be said, for otherwise the stranger would feel embarrassed at the end of the talk. It was Rincey who broke the silence.

The stranger had moved to the bar to get his glass of Guinness and so Rincey could now get a look at him without being obvious. He saw a man who was perhaps in his early thirties. He had a handsome and kindly face. His hand, which he stretched for the glass of Guinness, was slender and white, but a strong hand for all that, and there was a big scar in the back of the hand as if an operation had been performed on it. Rincey felt sorry that so fine a hand as that had had to be marred, and he felt a twinge of pity too, for the operation, he was sure, must have been very painful.

"It's grand weather we are having this day, God's blessing on it," said Rincey.

"Wonderful weather," said the stranger.

Again there was a little silence.

I was wrong then, Rincey thought. He'll be an Englishman. If he were an Irishman he would not be content to say it was wonderful weather, but would have gone on from there to talk of the hawthorn blooming like faith itself along the roadside, or he would mention some little thing he had seen—a red cow on a bright hill or a fox that crossed the road before him. And if he were an American he would say that the weather reminded him of California, or New York or wherever it was that he came from. But only an Englishman would say merely, "Wonderful weather," for the English were like nervous children in the world, afraid of being misunderstood or taken advantage of by strangers.

36

"You'll have come a long way no doubt," said Rincey.

"A long way," said the stranger. "But I have reached the end of my journey."

"Here in Killknock?" said Tim Conneeley, very surprised that a journey should end in Killknock, for the village was a place from which people started out. It was the starting point of journeys by the young men to the United States or to Australia or to Chile or to England. It was not a destination at all.

"Here in Killknock," said the stranger. "I have been meaning to come here for a long time. Sometimes I thought it might not be necessary. I thought that my business here would take care of itself. But it did not. And so I have come to attend to it personally." He was looking at Tom Joyce as he said this.

Everybody immediately wondered what the stranger's business might be because there was little business of any kind in Killknock. There was the fishing and a little farming and some road work but nothing that could be called business. Maybe he's from the IRA, thought Rincey. That would explain the scar on the back of his hand. Is there someone in the village that he would be gunning for? Would it be Dr. McEwan that's an Orangeman? Is that the reason why Dr. McEwan came here five years ago—to escape the IRA because of something he might have done to one of its members? And is the stranger here now to kill him? Or is it something that Tom Joyce did, that no one knows of?

He looked at the stranger's face—a sidelong look but a probing one. It was not the face of a killer. There was nothing hard about it, though there was a good deal of determination in it. There had been men killed in the village during the trouble; one had been a policeman. He'd died badly, crying like a child and tearing the uniform off himself and swearing that he would have nothing to do with the constabulary if they would just spare him. "I've a wife and three children," he had said. "A wife and three children living—" Whatever it was that he had intended to say about the three children had never been said for at that very moment the policeman had been shot. Rincey had shot him. Little Rincey who looked like a marmoset and was as gentle as a kitten. He had shot him because of the IRA man that the constabulary had found on Copul Beach, all alone and made naked by the space of the beach around him. He had nowhere to run but into the ocean and the police had come up on him from the two ends of the beach and from the landward side. They'd shot him as if he were a mad dog and he had fallen down and then got up and ran into the ocean as if running into eternity. When the water was up around his knees, they had shot him again and he had fallen down into the ocean and died there.

Rincey was old now and he felt sorry about the man who had been killed on the beach and the policeman he had killed himself in reprisal. He felt sorry because of the loneliness of their deaths. They had been swept out of

life without a touch of kindness to ease the parting—
the one running to the ocean for succor and the other
tearing off his uniform and talking of his wife and his
children. It was an awful way to die. Rincey carried this
sorrow with him through his life.

It seemed probable to Rincey then that the stranger
was from the IRA and recalling the look that Tom Joyce
had given him as he entered, he concluded that it was
Tom Joyce he was after.

While Rincey was thinking in this manner, Tim Conneeley plucked up his courage. "If you have business here
in Killknock, you'll be needing a place to stay, no
doubt?" he said.

"I will," said the stranger.

"There's the priest's house," said Tom Joyce, making
his first contribution to the conversation. He spoke almost hopefully, as if there would be some security for
him if the stranger stayed in the priest's house.

"I wouldn't like to disturb him," said the stranger.

"Well then there's Dr. McEwan," said Tim Conneeley. "He's from the Six Counties," he added. Tim had
concluded that if the man did not want to stay at the
priest's house it was because he was not a Catholic. The
mention of the Six Counties was a tactful way of convey-
ing the information that Dr. McEwan was a Protestant
and residence with him might be more to the stranger's
taste.

39

"I hardly think that that would be the place either," said the stranger.

He's a gunman for sure then, Rincey thought to himself. A gunman would not want to profane the priest's house and he would not want to stay in the house of an Orangeman.

"You would be welcome in my house," he said, blushing a little at making the offer, but made bold by anxiety. "It is no great place, but you would be as welcome there as my own son. I have a room that looks out over the bay and a good feather mattress on the bed, and—" he stopped because there was nothing more he could say in his desperation to have the stranger stay at his house.

"Thank you," said the stranger. "It is kind of you to offer me room. I would be glad of it."

Suddenly Rincey felt enormously happy. It was as if the weight of the terrible sin which he had committed so many years before had already been largely removed.

"It is you who are doing me the service, sir," he said. "It is you who are doing me the service. I believe this is the finest day in all the world," he continued, for he had to say something because of the elation within him.

"You are the second to say so today," said the stranger.

Tim Conneeley grinned vacuously at him, but Tom Joyce merely mumbled something and walked out through the door leaving half his glass of Guinness on the counter.

Chapter Four

THE next evening Tom Joyce went in his curragh to the place where Tim Conneeley had caught the eel. It was a rocky point off the island of Inishlacken. He waited until the moon was up, for eels are to be caught only by moonlight, the moon being their mother. They are born on moonlight nights and not in the sea but far from it in ponds and lakes well inland. When the moon comes up, and the eels are still tiny, they leave the ponds and slither in squirming shoals of tiny silver threads over the wet grass to the ocean which will be their home until they die.

He had seen such a migration of the eels once when he was a boy.

STRANGER AT KILLKNOCK

He had been out on the other side of Knockmaan and was coming home past the lake in which the boulders drank every year on the first of November. It had been dark, the stars too distant to put more than a frosting of light upon the land which lay under the shroud of night. He could see the head of Knockmaan against the sky and he was afraid of it.

The upper peak, where the boulders stood, after a while became gradually suffused with light and then, silently, and frightfully, the moon slid into the night sky over the mountain and a corpse-white light flowed over the lake and over the meadow that surrounded it. Then the surface of the lake had been disturbed by first one, then two, then a dozen, then a score and soon hundreds of small wriggling black lines which he had taken to be a cat's-paw of wind passing over it. But these little black lines had come from the lake to the shore and there, glistening like quicksilver, wriggled out by the thousands. There was such a multitude of them that when they reached the long wet grass of the meadow in which they disappeared they made it move as they passed through.

At the head of this elver host, summoned by the appearance of the moon from the depths of the lake, was a huge conger, perhaps as much as twelve or fifteen feet long. He was a wicked old bull of an eel and led the Lilliput army of elvers over the meadow until they came to the mountain. Here they all hesitated for a while, as if

42

in some obeisance to the mountain. Then they divided, swarming around its base, and uniting on the other side, made their way silently to the sea.

The sight so frightened him that he had spoken of it to no one.

Tom Joyce had in his curragh now the body of the dead eel. Tim Conneeley had thrown it upon the rocks, for although at one time it was possible to sell eels and get a good price for them, the market no longer existed. With the body of the dead eel he knew he could catch the other. Eels traveled in pairs when full grown and if one was killed, the other stayed in the area for some days, searching for its mate, slithering through the rocks and weeds, feared by all the other fishes; a shape at once of grace and of horror in the cold submarine tides of the ocean. There was no reason for him to catch the eel except that it amused him to do so. It would provide some excitement for him and he would have some time to think. He thought better on the ocean.

He picked up the long white corpse of the eel and dropped it into the sea and watched for a few seconds while it sank below in the dark water—a pale attenuated shape given the appearance of life by the movement of the waves on the surface. Then he reached behind him to the bow of the curragh and opened a tin box in which he kept his cigarettes. He took one out and feeling along the seam of his trouser leg, got hold of a safety pin which he kept there. He opened the pin and with the point

43

pierced the cigarette perhaps half an inch from the butt. He always did that. The moist air over the ocean swelled the tobacco in the cigarette and made it hard to draw. The hole made by the safety pin remedied the situation.

When the cigarette was lit, he rolled it to a corner of his mouth and baited the hook on the end of his line with a gobbet of fat bacon. He threaded it on in such a way that the rind on the bacon was clear of the barb of the hook and would not prevent its penetrating into the mouth of the eel when it took the bait. The moon was up now—not high in the sky, but clear of the horizon and enormously magnified by the density of the earth's atmosphere. A yellow moon, marked with dark areas, and a full moon too. It was the right moon for the job and he threw the hook into the water and fed the line out after it until he felt the lead sinker hit the bottom. Then he took a turn of the line around his fist and sat waiting, his body crouched forward a little and his elbows on his knees.

The surface of the ocean around him was sheeted with light from the moon, but near the curragh, where he looked down upon the ocean, it was dark. It seemed that he was floating in a pool of darkness, though surrounded by silver on the margin of this dark pool. This was the way a man spent his life—in a dark pool of his own, isolated from the light around, which he could see but which retreated as he approached it. All his effort was to get away from this isolation and loneliness, but it was without avail. He might know a hundred people or a thousand people, but all were strangers to him. They spoke and they laughed but these were mere sounds that came from them and did not for a moment diminish the isolation nor bridge the dark pool of the solitary being.

"It is a true thing," he mused to himself, "that the world was born with me and it will die with me. It did not exist for me before I opened my eyes and it will go forever the day I shut them for the last time. It is my world. I created it when I was born and I will destroy it when I die. Sorrow for the world then, the day I draw my last breath."

He liked the ocean at night. The very fact that you could not see far across it in the darkness increased its mystery. The silence of the world around—of the birds and of the noises made by men—the night silence emphasized the sounds of the ocean; the lapping of its tiny waves on the side of the curragh, the deeper splash of the bigger ones, the slight groan of the oars on the thole pins. All these small voices could be heard distinctly only at night and all of them he loved. The ocean, shapeless, enormous, powerful, was a being that awakened by night.

He thought about the stranger who had come to the village. The first glimpse he had had of the stranger as he came into Feeney's bar with the light behind him, had filled him with unease. Why should that be? He had never seen the man before. The uneasiness was deep and he searched his mind for the cause of it, or for something to liken it to, which would give him some hint of the cause of it. Well, it was like the uneasiness that came when a secret, long hid, is about to be exposed.

He had such a secret. It concerned the time of the White Storm and the boy who had been with him and had been drowned. They had been four miles off the coast taking in a mackerel net that he had set in a tide run. There was a whiteness all around—in the sky and on the ocean and in the curragh, and he remembered even now that it made the boy's face white and his arms also and showed up on the gunwales like the touch of a ghost and on the oars and on every upturned surface. The boy was frightened of it and kept saying his Rosary. Once he stopped in his task of hauling the curragh along the headrope and said, "We should go in now, Tom Joyce, and leave the net, for there is an uneasiness in the weather and if we do not, we will never make shore again."

"I will not go in until we have been through the net and taken the few fish that there are in it," said Tom.

"Then we are dead men," said the boy.

"You are a fool for saying it," said Tom. And so they had gone the length of the net taking perhaps forty fish out of it and had turned the curragh for Killknock, steering by the mountain, when the storm broke.

It came first with little puffs and scurries of wind while the sky darkened and the water darkened with it.

The area of the wind, where it struck the water, might be no more than ten yards long and the same in width. But it whipped the surface into a white froth where it struck. The wind didn't come from out toward the west nor from the east or south but from straight above; or so it seemed. One of these cat's-paws struck the curragh and flattened her down in the water as if to founder her from the very force of the blow.

Then there came the sound of the storm. It was first a deep rumble like thunder and Tom looked westward and saw a line of white on the dark ocean out toward the horizon.

"Holy Mother of God," cried the boy, staring at it. The rumble persisted but above it came a hiss like a thousand kettles steaming on a fire. And above and beyond that noise, there was a scream, very high and tiny to start with but waxing louder with each second. That was the real wind, Tom knew. The rumble was the waves— great walls of water that fled before the storm. The hiss was the lashed sea that followed, unable to form waves because of the fierceness of the wind over it. And the shriek was the wind itself.

It was death to head for shore now. The big waves, outriders of the gale, would be upon them and roll the curragh over if she were not put head toward them. So he spun the curragh around, yelling to the boy to throw out the fish and get the bailer. But the boy could not move from fear and sat in the stern, facing him, and help-less.

Tom reached over and struck him with his fist—a hard jarring blow on the side of the boy's face that knocked him nearly off his seat.

"Throw out the fish," he shouted. "Get the bailer."

Then the first of the big waves were on them. He met it head on and worked with the oars, sinking them deep into the flank of the wave and putting his shoulders and back into the stroke. He had to move the curragh up the wave faster than the water was rolling down or the wave would take her. She rose like a bird, higher and higher. As he went up he could look down on the boy and he knew he was being taken higher on the back of the wave than had ever happened to him before.

The bottom of his stomach was a pit of fear at the height they were going and the terrible drop there would be beyond. He was afraid mostly of the crest of the wave, however, the foaming crest where the strength of the wave was. It could flip them over like a straw, end over end if he did not meet it just right. It would roll them down the side of the wave and they could be drowned in the huge body of it without a cry. He glanced for one second behind and up and saw the crest above him and heaved on the oars and the curragh went through the crest like an eel through weeds. Then down, plunging into the valley that lay between this first wave and the mountain of water behind it. And still the boy

48

was not bailing and had not thrown out the fish. The water was up to their knees and he shouted to the boy to bail but without response.

The curragh had to be lightened and in that moment the boy recovered some of his courage and started to work with the bailer. He threw the fish out with one hand and worked the bailer with the other. But he was too frightened to work fast and the water was deeper and the curragh more sluggish when she hit the crest of the second wave. She had to be lightened immediately, for she could not survive a third wave heavy and slow as she was.

They were reaching the trough between the waves when Tom threw the boy over. It was easily done. He was a thin light lad and he was reaching forward with the bailer. The curragh, set off balance by the shifting of his weight, had for a moment tipped to one side and Tom leaned toward the boy and pushed him on the shoulder. The boy was gone into the roaring water in a second. The fury around was so great, the noise of the sea and the wind so thunderous, that he made no audible splash, and only as much disturbance in the water as would be made by a tiny pebble being thrown into the margin of the sea.

The third wave was on the curragh and her head had to be kept to it and she must be driven up the sides toward the ugly crest above, using all the strength of his arms and his back and his shoulders. Tom could not spare a moment of regret for the boy but he saw his face before he went under and it was full of fear.

Lightened by the boy's weight the curragh rode more easily up the wave and though hesitating for a terrible moment in the crest, still went through and down the other side, and then, alone in the gale, he had battled for his life.

He had contrived a sea anchor out of a steering oar and his jacket and a piece of rope and put it overboard, making it fast to the forward seat so that the boat was kept roughly with her head to the wind and the battering of the ocean. In the gale itself there were no great waves but only a terrible welter of water and it was as if the ocean had risen into the air so that wind and water were one, embodying in this a fury implacable and against which no living creature could prevail. All this fury was directed at him—at him alone in the world, caught away from his fellow men, without aid or succor. The roaring wind and the boiling thundering water made a toy of his life.

The white layer of cloud which had preceded the storm for three days had now gone and in the sky above the moon was a hard round merciless light which made the ocean more terrible. At times huge spumes of spray flung upon him so that he could not breathe and always the spray stormed at him like hail, so that he could feel the clout of it even through his bawneen.

Soon it was useless to bail. His puny bailer could do

nothing to relieve the curragh of water but he knew that she would float, even swamped, and he might live if he could stay in her and keep her headed to the storm. It was the wood of the curragh only that supported the craft—the thin laths that ran forward from her stern to her bow, the wood of the gunwale and of the seats. The canvas of her sides would sink but the wood could support him and the weight of the water. But remaining in the curragh demanded all his skill and strength. Most of the time she was completely submerged, for she could not float on the scud which covered the ocean to a depth of a foot. Sometimes she went down below the solid water and he held to the seat, going down with her until his head was submerged. But he knew that if he let go, she would be gone from him and he could not live in this sea without her.

To cling to her the better, he turned, facing forward, wedging his body under the stern seat and holding on to the forward seat with his arms crooked around it. In this way there were long intervals when, under the water, he could not draw a breath. But he held on hour after hour.

Then he saw the boy.

For one second his head and shoulders were clear of the welter of foam and he caught a glimpse of the boy's body ahead of the boat. He saw just an arm raised up toward the sky, stark in the moonlight, and the white face of the boy and then he was again submerged.

The sight filled him with a terror distinct from his fear of the storm. The boy had become a corpse-watcher. He was waiting for him, his shipmate, to die. The fact that the body was there was a sure sign that he, Tom Joyce, must drown too.

He saw the boy several times after that, always ahead of the boat, never getting any nearer, sometimes with an arm raised, sometimes head and shoulders out of the water, once with only the foot showing, a thin little naked foot like a piece of bone in the moonlight. Then he came to understand that the boy was entangled in the sea anchor. But he was still a corpse-watcher. The storm had played this grim jest upon him, swirling the boy's body through the water until it had become entangled in the line of the sea anchor where it would serve to warn him of how he too would soon be drowned and white and cold in the ocean.

At the memory of this ordeal, he shuddered and jerked the line which he had wrapped around his fist all this time, and felt it heavy. The eel. He had almost forgotten about the eel. The eel he was fishing for was certainly on the line, for he could feel the weight of it, and an eel did not fight on a line like a fish but curled itself around its own body and up the line in its anger and pain.

He started pulling the line in hand over hand and when the hook broke the water he let out a great cry and threw it back and let the line slip out of the boat so that it was lost in the ocean.

For what was on the hook was the dead eel that he had thrown down to bring its mate.

He had fished for the living and caught the dead.

The sign was unmistakable. The stranger had come about the boy he had drowned in the White Storm.

Chapter Five

FATHER DIMMOCK was concerned about the appearance of the stranger in Killknock but he did not go to visit him, and that for a number of reasons. In the first place there was a certain protocol involved. It was the part of the stranger to visit the priest—unless of course he were of the Protestant faith. If he were a Protestant, then he would not of course visit the priest at his house, and he might resent the priest calling upon him.

If, on the other hand, the man were a Catholic who had fallen away from his faith without actively adopting any other, then the priest had to be careful of how he made contact with him. Fallen-away Catholics, as they were called, were astonishingly sensitive about priests. They felt guilty and defensive in their presence. Father Dimmock did not want that kind of reaction.

Curious as he was about the stranger, and anxious that he should have no ill effect upon the villagers over whom he was the shepherd, he decided that he would wait until the stranger called upon him, or some circumstance arose which would bring them together—a circumstance which would not be openly engineered.

In any case when the stranger arrived, the priest was on a visit into the mountains, where there was a quarrel between two families that had come to his attention and that he was afraid would breed bad blood.

The life in the mountain country, seven or eight miles from the coast, in the valleys of the bleak and stony mountains, was exceedingly lonely. There was nothing for the people to do but tend their sheep and their small acreages on which they raised the vegetables for their tables. The mountain people were separated from the village by a stretch of bogland perhaps four miles wide. On the near side of this bogland was the village with its solitary mountain, higher than all the others around. On the other side, a smaller range of mountains rose, like ocean waves, the one peeping over the shoulder of the other and so on for an extent of seventeen miles. It was a wild and brooding place of sudden mists and rains, and quick and enchanting sunlight, and gloom and purling clouds which now hid and now revealed the peaks and valleys around. On the peaks of some of the mountains there were grim solitary stones standing against the skyline. Some had faint whirls carved in them. Some had holes bored through them. No one knew for certain who had put them there.

When, tending their sheep, the mountain dwellers had to go by one of these cairns, they were careful to pick a piece of sally grass, a piece of heather and a round pebble and hold these in their hands. With these for protection, no harm would come to them. But if they neglected to secure these safeguards, then they might fall and break a bone, or be stricken with rheumatism, or have one of their sheep die, or be carried off and never be seen on the earth again. The sally grass represented a sword and warned that the bearer should not be harmed. The piece of heather was a flower offering—a token that the bearer came in peace. And the round stone? There was something connected with the stone that was dark and none of the mountain people would admit that they carried a round stone in their hands when they went close to the standing stones. But they did, nonetheless. Even the priest could not divine the significance of the round pebble that had to be carried. However adroitly he questioned the mountain dwellers—the Joyces and Walshes and O'Flahertys—he was met with evasions or protestations of ignorance. But at times he had an uneasy feeling that there was something close to idolatry among the people of the mountain valleys which had survived sixteen hundred years of Christian teaching.

The quarrel which brought Father Dimmock into the mountains on the day of the arrival of the stranger was between a man named Walsh and a brother and sister— Brid and Dermot O'Flaherty. The priest had heard of it from several sources, the most reliable being Tom Curtin who served as constable in the village and who knew most of what was going on around. The constable said it might lead to blows and so the priest came as peace-maker.

The O'Flahertys lived together in the shambles of a cottage—a thing of a single room with a sleeping loft above under the rotting thatch of the roof. The house was well over a hundred years old and built of loose lime-stones. Its walls were sagging so that the roof was at an angle, like a tam-o'-shanter put carelessly upon the head. Brother and sister were unkempt and tall, with pale blue eyes and big bones and rough gray hair. The man kept his hair hacked short, but the woman let hers grow and it was like the mane on a horse down her back whenever she took off her shawl.

These two seldom spoke to each other though they lived under the same roof. It was said that there were times when they had gone a month without exchanging a word. They knew precisely the routine of each day. There was no need for talk. All topics had been long exhausted to the point of fruitlessness. They found nothing new to talk about. They seemed indeed to be able to communicate without speech; and the woman, Brid, had an attitude toward her brother as if he were her father. Whenever they came down to the village they were hand in hand—not like lovers but like father and child. In Killknock it was said that Dermot and Brid O'Flaherty were out of their senses. Their minds had been taken from them, had seeped out of them, as it were, in the mists and gloom of the mountains.

The priest found them working side by side in their potato patch. The woman was weeding and the man was spraying the potatoes with a copper sulphate solution— it was called bluestone—to kill off the blight that would certainly destroy the crop if it were not sprayed.

The woman saw the priest first, coming suddenly into view above a little knoll that fronted their cottage, and she looked fearfully at her brother but went on with her weeding. The brother, though no word had been said, turned and saw the priest and looked angrily at him. He was not angry because it was the priest but because his isolation was disturbed. Then he collected himself and said in Irish, "God's blessing on you, Father, that you come to my house."

"God's and Mary's blessing on you, Dermot O'Fla-herty and your sister," said the priest.

The woman gave another look at her brother and he nodded his head sharply and she turned and went to the cottage.

"Come inside and rest, Father," he said. "Herself will have tea for you in this moment."

"Thank you," said the priest. "Your potatoes look well, I think."

"They will all die," said the man in a rush, "Peter Walsh has put a curse on them and on my sheep too. There are two sheep dead already. And there is a lamb dead, too."

He said this in a wild manner, like a man who had for a long time refrained from mentioning a grave injury until at last it burst from him almost against his will. He did not look at the priest as he spoke but to the mountains around and it seemed to Father Dimmock that he was talking to them rather than to him; calling on them to bear witness to the grave injuries from which he suffered.

The priest did not say anything immediately but went with the man into the one room of their house. It was not tidily kept as are the interiors of most cottages. The floor was of packed earth but it had not been swept in some time and there was a delft milk jug on the table which was dirty down the sides, raising his doubts as to the cleanliness of the milk it contained. There was not much in the room: a hearth for a fireplace on which a sullen peat fire burned; a deal table with two wooden chairs by it and two other chairs beside the hearth—one a rocking chair and the other little more than a stool, for it had no back. The woman, Brid, made a pot of tea on the hearth and the priest was made to sit in the rocking chair while he took the cup that she gave him and accepted also a slice of buttered soda bread for which he was grateful, for the climb up the mountain side had put an edge on his appetite.

He did not like the cottage. It was not merely the slovenliness of the place, distasteful as that was. But there was about it, about this wild unkempt man and his equally wild and unkempt sister, something repellent. It was the feeling a man had in the presence of the insane or the heavily crippled; a feeling that mere association with them might in some way affect him with their condition. Father Dimmock glanced at the light of perpetual adoration burning on the mantelpiece. He should have got some reassurance from it but he didn't. It seemed to be just a badge or perhaps a disguise for the real worship of this man and his sister.

He put the train of thought out of his mind with some effort and turned to the purpose of his visit. "I have heard there is bad blood between you and your cousin, Peter Walsh," he said. "Now what is the reason for it?"

"What is the reason for it?" echoed the man, in a high-pitched voice that seemed to be on the edge of hysteria. "What reason but that he is killing my sheep by putting a curse upon them."

"You should be ashamed to talk such nonsense," said the priest sharply. "It is not possible to kill a sheep by putting a curse on it."

At this the man and his sister exchanged looks as if they possessed knowledge beyond the ability of the priest to understand.

"As a Christian and a Catholic you should know better than to talk about superstitions like cursing sheep to kill them," the priest reiterated sharply.

"The sheep are dead," said the man sullenly. "They are floating in the little lake at this moment, all swelled up like bladders."

"What lake?" asked the priest.

"What lake but the Lake of the Stones?" said the man in his high-pitched, quarrelsome voice. "He put a drowning curse on them and they were taken to the lake during the night and drowned in it and that is all there is to it."

"You are talking nonsense," said the priest sharply. "It is sinful to talk in this manner. The sheep wandered during the night and got mired in the mud of the lake where they went to drink and were drowned. There can be no other explanation."

"Well, isn't it a strange thing that the sheep were healthy three days ago and it was then that Peter Walsh put the drowning curse on them? And isn't it a strange thing that that very night they were drowned and no other night? And now he says he will drown my sister and she is in fear of her life from him."

The priest looked at the woman. She did indeed seem to be afraid. There was the brightness of fear in her eyes and she made the sign of the cross rapidly three times, which annoyed the priest, for it was not made from devotion but from superstition.

"What have you done to Peter Walsh that he should be angry with you?" demanded Father Dimmock.

"What have I done?" cried the man, looking wildly about and rocking his head from side to side as he did so. "I have done nothing to him at all."

"What does he say you have done to him?" persisted the priest.

"He says my sheep are grazing in his field. But it is not true. My sheep stay in my own field. I have good stones in the walls and they cannot jump over them. And the gate is never left open. And his fields have worse grazing than mine so why would I let my sheep into his field? He made a cross of two sticks and put it outside my gate and said that I would soon be buried under it."

The priest understood the trouble. The loneliness of the mountain life made every incident, however trivial, important. A sheep straying into a neighbor's field was taken not as an accident, but as an act deliberately planned and with malicious intent. The mountain people had to have something to vent their anger on. They could not vent it on the weather nor the mountains nor the grim solitary stones on the mountain tops. They were afraid of these things. So they vented it on each other. Plainly Dermot O'Flaherty's sheep had strayed to the lake and been drowned in it. And Peter Walsh, knowing this before O'Flaherty, had pretended to put what was

called the drowning curse on the sheep. Or perhaps Peter Walsh had had his dog cut out the sheep from O'Flaherty's flock and chase them into the lake. That was more likely. He would see Peter Walsh and deal sternly with him. But he would deal just as sternly with O'Flaherty and his sister.

"I do not want to hear of any trouble between you and Peter Walsh," he said rising. "Stay away from the man for the time being and keep your sheep in your own enclosures. And do not let me hear any more nonsense about this cursing of sheep. You disgrace yourselves with that kind of talk. I think the two of you are too idle and that is what breeds the trouble. Bridget O'Flaherty, you would be better off if you kept your house in better order. It is well known that the devil fears to enter a tidy home. And Dermot O'Flaherty, if you will go about your farm and mend your walls where the stones have been knocked down, you will lose no more sheep."

"My walls are in good repair," said the man.

"I crossed gaps in two of them without jumping or climbing," said the priest.

"I am afraid of Peter Walsh," said the woman, speaking for the first time. "He has put the drowning curse on me and I am afraid of him."

"If you came to Mass on Sundays and went to confession more often, you would not be subject to these superstitions which are nothing but the whisperings of Satan," replied the priest.

"You do not know what it is to live in the mountains," said the woman fiercely. "You are down there in the village and in the church and things are different down there. But in the mountains there are Things you do not know of in the village. For three nights there has been the fairy fire on the bogs. Last night we heard the dog howling and when my brother called to him to be quiet, he howled all the more. And when my brother went to the door he could see the dog running across his field and everywhere he put his paws down there were four marks of fire. That is something you do not know about in the church. And when my brother went out in the morning, the shape of the mountain had changed."

She said all this with vehemence and at a great speed as if she had only a certain amount of time in which to get it all out. But she spoke as if someone outside the cottage might be listening to her.

"What do you mean, the shape of the mountain had changed?" asked the priest.

Brother and sister looked at each other and now it was the brother who spoke—still wildly but again as if he were afraid someone might be listening to their conversation.

"You know that there are two bullans on the mountain behind us, Father?" he asked. "They are called Carraig Fear and Carraig Bean—the Man Stone and the Woman Stone. The one is fifteen feet tall and the other is twelve and the Woman Stone has a hole through it, and if you put your hand through the hole there will be a child born in your house that year, and if you put the head of a ewe in it, she will have good lambs. . . ."

"Yes, yes," said the priest testily. "But why do you say the shape of the mountain has changed?"

"Aren't I coming to that as fast as I can?" said Dermot. "When I went out this morning the bullans were not standing there any more."

"Not standing?" echoed the priest.

"They were not standing," repeated Dermot. He looked at his sister and talking to her rather than the priest, he said, "They had tipped forward on the mountain so that from this house you cannot see them against the sky and so they have changed the shape of the mountain."

"It is the thirst that is in them," said the woman fearfully. "They are going to the lake for a drink."

"But that is not until the night of the first of November," said the priest sharply and before he could think of what he was saying. "It is only the middle of May."

"The stones will move early this year down to the lake," said the woman. "From the tops of the mountain they will come down to the valley to the lake in throngs —hobbling and lumbering down and shaking the ground. The stones are angry at something that has happened in the village. Someone in the village will be turned into a stone for what he has done."

"I forbid you to think, let alone talk this kind of nonsense," stormed the priest. "Have you no respect for me that you talk sheer idolatry in my presence? Is this the kind of thing that is going on in my parish?" And then, because of his anxiety on this point, he said ludicrously, "What would Dr. McEwan say if he heard of this among Catholics?"

With that he went—glad enough to be away; angry, and not in the least sure that he had shaken the minds of the O'Flahertys or done the slightest good in healing the breach between them and Peter Walsh.

But he was too wild against the man and his sister to be concerned that he had not achieved the object of his mission. They were stupid and ignorant and superstitious and pagan and there was nothing that could be done with them. His Irish temper fumed within him and he vowed that he'd report the two of them to the bishop. Then he decided that he would not, for the bishop would say that it was the priest's job to get rid of all these superstitions and it was a disgrace that they should still persist in any parish in Ireland. What did the bishop, in his fine house in the city, know of the people of the mountains? What did the bishop know of the mountains, for that matter? He got a view of them from his car on the highroad when he came to the village once a year to give Confirmation. That was all. They were something on a picture postcard for the bishop. . . . Just a piece of scenery.

When these angry thoughts had run through his mind

Father Dimmock felt a bit better, for his temper, though violent, was short and he always felt miserable and repentant afterwards. If he failed to make heaven it would be because of his temper. His mother had told him so as a boy and he still believed this. He was sorry for his anger immediately and turned, half thinking that he should go back to the O'Flaherty cottage and see whether he could not, using a milder tone, get them to see reason.

Beyond their cottage the head of the mountain rose facing the head of the Mountain of Mananaan. And the shape of the mountain had certainly changed. The two bullans no longer stood against the sky and although, compared with the mass of the mountain, they were tiny indeed, yet their absence made a strange difference in the outline of the mountain, as if it had been flattened down by having sunk into the ground.

He decided against going back to the cottage. He had come too far down the mountain side and besides he had his dignity to consider. The O'Flahertys deserved to be chastised and he had chastised them. But he was sorry for his angry thoughts about the bishop, who was a much holier and wiser man than himself. The repentance was as genuine as the anger. It made a wrench at his heart to realize how weak he was in the face of his own temper. He went on down the mountain, chastened.

When he had set out it had been a beautiful day. Now suddenly, the sun was gone. A fine white mist poured down the valley upon him—cold and mysterious and obscuring all around. He had to grope his way through it down to the road and every now and then the sudden appearance of a rock or a twisted hawthorn bush would give him a shock, for it seemed that it was not he who moved toward these things but they that moved toward him.

He heard, from farther up the valley, the whimper of the wind and then, from in front of him, came the hiss and splash of water. He thought of the stones bobbling down the mountain toward the lake and involuntarily he glanced behind him and crossed himself.

When he got back to the priest's house in the village, his housekeeper told him that a stranger had arrived in the village, and was staying at Rincey the cobbler's.

"He has business in the village," she said. "And he has a great gift of healing, for he can cure the deaf."

"He can what?" demanded the priest.

"Feeney, that keeps the public house, is not deaf any more," said the housekeeper. "The deafness left him when the stranger walked into his house."

"Nonsense," snorted the priest. "I'll take a cup of tea before the fire. The day has turned a little soft."

"It has turned soft indeed," said the housekeeper, "and there are people who will tell you that next month will be the month of June. And so it will be on the calendar. But I have lived around these parts a long time, and judging from the weather, I tell you the next month will not be June at all but November—the Month of the Stones."

And with that she left the room, leaving the priest staring after her.

Chapter Six

THE day after he arrived in the village, the stranger said that he would go out and look at the sea. Rincey the cobbler believed that by this he meant he would stroll over to the sea wall overlooking the harbor and spend some time sunning himself there and looking idly at the water, listening to the minuscule murmur of the tide as it crept into the harbor, covering tiny pebbles centimeter by centimeter, stirring the seaweed which clung breathless in the sun to the larger rocks, sending the little crabs scurrying with delight along the harbor bottom, and raising the pucans very gradually so that they would no longer lie on their sides but would after an hour take life, as it were, and float upon the deepened water.

It was a great sight this, the incoming of the tide, one which never failed to move the villagers. The youngest of them and the oldest of them found it full of wonder, as if it were the great bosom of God that was moving before their eyes. The little boys and girls would get down into the harbor splashing around among the rocks on the slippery seaweed looking for the many treasures which an outcoming tide uncovered or an incoming tide brought with it. There was always something new—a little silver fish caught in a pool, or a shell coated thick with mother-of-pearl to set them thinking of the Indies and the pearl divers there, or a sea anemome to poke so that it jetted water sulkily at its attacker, or the cast-off shell of a large crab or maybe a lead sinker lodged in the rocks, and removed, with great excitement and cries of "It's mine. It's mine. I saw it first!"

Surely the world could contain no greater excitements than the bottom of the harbor at Killknock. It was the greatest place to be when the water was low, and there was a special thrill to it because you could look up and far above your head see on the harbor breakwater the height that the ocean reached when the tide was full. It was like walking about under the sea then and that was thrilling in itself.

The older people too liked to be down at the harbor wall when the tide turned. They would gather there at the turn and lean on the wall and watch it. How slow it was and how strong and resistless. It was measured first in the gradual wetting and then submersion of pebbles. Then the inflowing water changed the direction of the seaweed. The outcoming tide left the weed streaming like the hair of the ocean out to sea. The incoming tide took these huge hanks of weed and slowly, gently turned them toward land again. There was a tinkling sound to the inward creeping of the water. It was like tiny bells being rung. And there was also a sad sighing sound as the weed turned landward over the rocks.

The ebb tide was sad.

When men died, they died in the ebb tide. The soul went out of them as the water receded. If they could last through the ebb, then the strength would come back to them while the tide was on the make. The tides of the ocean were a clock for the lives of men. They were old and unfailing.

Rincey then thought that the stranger would be going to watch the tide come in by the sea wall and he asked if his daughter, Mairin, could go with him.

Rincey was sixty years of age but Mairin was only seven. That was not uncommon in Killknock. Rincey had not married until he was in his fifties and his wife had died a few weeks after the child was born. She had been a delicate girl of twenty with a dreamy look to her as if she was not much in the world at all. The child was like her mother—fair-haired, blue-eyed, slight, with a skin as white as the inside of orange peel, and so lightly boned that Rincey was all the time frightened that she would, in running about, break some part of herself.

He loved the child deeply.

Caitlin the Other House had helped him rear the baby until he had the knack of it himself. And then he had turned down all offers of help and looked after her by himself.

Some of the women in the village gave him clothes for her and for a while he accepted these and gladly. But then he decided the other people's clothes were not for Mairin. She must have her own and they must be new. And he had gone to the terrible expense of buying new clothes for her whenever they were needed, and would not take clothes that other children had grown out of. She was a princess then, and was to wear no other's garments.

He did not treat her completely as a child but sometimes as an equal. When he was vexed in his mind about whether to do something or not, he would talk the matter over with his slight and angel-like little daughter. She listened very seriously to him and tried to advise him. And he listened equally seriously to what she had to say and sometimes took her advice. Nor was she spoiled by his deep love for her. She had no temper fits. And if, as sometimes happened, Rincey spoke sharply to her, being angered by some little thing, she would put her hands to her face to hide from his anger and cry, very quietly.

73

He could not stay angry with her long and upbraided himself for many hours afterward that he had been vexed with her.

The two went off together then, the stranger and Mairin, and Rincey set to work to mend a pair of boots for the priest and another pair for Curtin the policeman. But the stranger did not go to the harbor but turned up the village and went with Mairin over the hill past the church and under the shadow of the head of the mountain, which he stopped and looked at for a little while in silence, and so on to Copul Beach a mile and a half away.

Once out of the village the road became little more than a boreen. An attempt had been made to pave it in part with crushed stones and tar, but this was mere patchwork and its surface consisted in the main of dust and earth and hard ridges of limestone rock. There was a wall of loose stones on either side, and between the road and the wall the grass grew deep, and in places the wall was almost covered by grasses or by the verdant cool fronds of bracken or by the long entwining brambles of blackberries which were covered with small white flowers so that there would be a good crop of berries in the latter part of the summer. Mairin and the stranger walked in silence for a while and it was she who opened the conversation.

"You must never be afraid of a white goose," she said. "They will do you no harm at all."

"I am glad to hear it," said the stranger.

"A white goose jumped at me once," said Mairin. "And I was afraid. But Himself took a stick to it and it went off hissing like an old kettle."

"Himself?" asked the stranger.

"Mr. Rincey, himself," said Mairin patiently.

"There are four swans in Ireland that are the daughters of an old king," said Mairin, after a little silence. "If you find one of them, they'll make you into a swam yourself."

"It would be nice to be a swan," said the stranger.

"Arrah it would and it wouldn't," said Mairin. "It would be nice to be a swan if you were a swan but it wouldn't be nice to be a swan if you were a king's daughter."

"That's true enough," said the stranger.

"There were a lot of kings in Ireland long ago and the Rinceys were kings of them all," said Mairin. "They lived in a palace with a wall of ebony around it. The wall was so big that if you started out around it when you were very small, you would be as old as Himself when you got back to where you started from. How old do you think Himself is?"

To this the stranger did not reply but looked with sorrow at Mairin as if he knew something which she would find out and would bring her grief. But Mairin did not really want an answer to her question because she said almost immediately, "It was the English who killed

75

off all the kings in Ireland. They killed the kings first and then they killed the princes and the princesses. Then they killed the nobles and those that were left turned themselves into geese and flew away from Ireland, some to Gaul and some to Spain.

"When the end of the world comes, England will be burned up with fire but Ireland will be covered by the tide of the sea."

"Who told you this?" asked the stranger.

"Himself," was the reply.

They went on in silence together, the little girl busy with her own world which was full of white swans and kings and the tales of hermits and saints and holy nuns, and the stranger walking beside her smiling at the glint of the sunlight in her hair and the delicate line of her little chin and neck and the suppleness of her figure and the way she had of amusing herself with everything they came upon.

Thus she would hop at times on one leg and then on the other and then she would do a little skipping jump and then, somewhat bored by the view walking forward and seeing all coming toward her, she would turn around and walk backward to see how things looked when they went away from her. She seemed to miss nothing in the world about her but to be acutely aware of all that was going on, so that when a skylark rose from a little field and went up into the sky until it was lost from view she stood to watch it and then to listen to the song of the bird which could no longer be seen in the blueness above. And when she heard a grasshopper in some long grass she stopped and went slowly into the grass and returned in a minute or two with the grasshopper held in her hand like a jade carving. And when a puff of wind raised a little cloud of dust on the road she smiled with pleasure at the sudden rising of the dust into the air and when they came to a clump of wild rose she said that there was a poet buried there.

"What was his name?" asked the stranger.

"How would I know?" asked Mairin. "Sure he was dead hundreds of years before I was born. But a wild rose will grow on the grave of any poet and that is how you know where they are buried. There are more wild roses in Ireland than anywhere else in the world."

"I suppose Himself told you," said the stranger.

"The same," said Mairin.

Finally they turned down an even smaller road and crossed two stiles and found themselves on a low and undulating headland where the turf was thick and grew close to the ground. It was like a thick mantle spreading over it and the stranger sat down to rest on the turf with below him a wide crescent of white sandy beach. He found then that the turf did not consist of short grass but of scores of little plants. Some were like clover and some like vetch and some like silverweed, but they were all on the smallest scale and they put out flowers whose size was little bigger than the head of a pin. These miniature blossoms, pink and blue and gold and white, could be seen only when the turf was looked at closely. The over-all impression was of a lush green, but it was the pinpoints of blossom in the green that gave it a depth and sparkle— so that the turf was like one would imagine it to be in Heaven.

The stranger was so delighted with it that he lay down full length on his back, as if to press himself as closely as possible to it; as if he had been long away from it and having now found it again, wished to embrace it and bring it as close to his body as he could to make up for the time he had been away.

"I am going down to the sand to find a shrimp and whatever else I can find," said Mairin. "I will be yonder in the rocks." The stranger did not reply and off she went; and with the warmth of the sun and the pleasant-ness of the breeze and the loveliness of the cloud shadows passing over him as cool as a blessing, he was soon asleep.

Mairin went down the sand cliff which was but ten or fifteen feet high to the beach and then ran to one end of it where there were some rocks, and climbed up a big table of a rock where she knew where would be a pool of water left by the receding tide. It was shallow in one end and deep at the other and she went into it in the shallow end, pulling up the hem of her dress and de-lighted to see how the water seemed to bend that portion of her legs which were immersed in it.

She put her hand in and noticed that her arm was bent

just below where it entered the water and was delighted at this because it was an exciting thing to have happen. She tucked her skirt into her pants so as to have her hands free and walked slowly into the deeper part of the pool watching for a little spurt of sand on the bottom which would betray the presence of a shrimp.

She spent a long time hunting them in the pool and caught seven but three got away.

Then she went off to another pool that lay farther out and found there two big sea anemomes and a green crab and a leathery oblong thing with a vinelike growth on each corner which she knew was the egg of a dogfish or perhaps a shark.

A white herring gull flung out of the sky upon her so close that she could hear the silky rustle of the wind in its wings and she watched it soar with easy grace up into the sunlight before it dived again and, striking the water, rose with a small herring which it had gobbled down in a minute. When the herring had been eaten the gull floated on the surface of the water for a while and then took off, but had some difficulty becoming airborne because of the size of the fish it had eaten.

So the time went by and the girl played and the stranger slept and the tide came in. Mairin only noticed that the tide had been flowing for over an hour when she looked for her handkerchief in which she had tied the shrimps she had caught.

She had put it on a rock nearby, and a little lower

from the one on which she had climbed looking for peri-
winkles. Now neither rock nor handkerchief were there.
The ocean had washed over them.

The various rocks on which she had come out from the
beach were lost under the water or showed only in a
wash of white and she was cut off.

She was immediately panicked, for she could not swim
and the tide which was now in its full flow was swirling
fast around the rock on which she stood. The sound of
it, until a minute before, had been pleasant and musical
to her. But now it filled her with terror.

Far away on the headland she could see the stranger,
still flat on his back and asleep as she had left him. She
shouted to him but her voice was lost in the sounds of
the sea and when she had shouted several times she began
to whimper like a little animal and then to cry.

She could not do anything to save herself. If she
ventured into the water, she would be knocked off her
feet and drowned and if she stayed where she was, she
would be drowned too, for at full tide the rock on which
she stood was five feet below the water.

When she had cried for a while she tried shouting
again, but the noise of the waves drowned her voice and
made her feel all the more abandoned and helpless.

The waves were getting bigger as the water deepened
with each minute and one, smashing into the base of the
rock on which she stood, threw a heavy spray over it so
that she was drenched. At that she shouted again to the

stranger and waved her arms to attract his attention. While she was doing this, with her back to the ocean, a larger wave burst on the rock. The spray came solidly over it and hit her in the back and she lost her balance and fell from the rock into the water.

She clawed with her hands to get a grip of the seaweed on the rock and her head went down in the ocean and she could feel the seaweed mixing with her hair. She got a grip of the seaweed but it was slippery and another wave came as she tried to pull herself to the rock and tore her away from it.

She got her head above the surface but a dollop of water hit her mouth and some got into her throat and made her cough. She gasped for air and got only water and then went down into the sea, not struggling very hard but in pain and fright.

After a while she found that she was lying on the turf and the stranger was leaning over her. He did not look at all troubled or concerned, but rather serene and a little amused.

"You were sleeping and I shouted to you and waved and I could have drowned," Mairin said and she broke into tears.

"You are safe now," said the stranger. "Do not think about it."

"Did you save me?"

"Yes. I heard you calling and saved you. You should

81

not have gone so far out. But you would have been safe anyway. I was watching out for you."

"You were sleeping."

"Yes. But I saved you anyway."

She sat up and looked at him, still resentful. "Your clothes are not even wet," she said. She looked him over closely from head to foot. He was barefooted and busy now putting on his socks. Suddenly she was not angry any more.

"I know who you are," she said. "You are not a stranger at all."

"I'm glad you know," said the stranger. "But do not tell anyone else. I want them to find out for themselves."

"Can't I even tell Himself?" she asked.

"No," said the stranger.

He rose and extended a hand to her and they went slowly over the turf of the headland back toward the boreen.

Mairin remembered the sea gull that had swooped down on her and soared so beautifully up into the sky. "I wish I could fly like a sea gull," she said.

"That is for sea gulls but not for little girls. But if you like I will carry you," the stranger replied.

He bent down and lifted her up and it seemed to her that she was flying anyway, he moved so smoothly along.

Chapter Seven

UNTIL the coming of the stranger and the catching of the dead eel when he had been fishing for a live one, Tom Joyce had not given any thought to the murder of the boy in his curragh during the White Storm.

Indeed, he did not think of the deed as murder at any time, but as an act which it had been necessary for him to perform to preserve his boat and, with it, his own life.

Had he been washed overboard the boy would not have been saved. The boy was useless on the water and would not have known how to rig a sea anchor and, by keeping the curragh's head to the storm, prevent the boat from being turned over.

He would have panicked and been drowned. And if the boy had stayed in the curragh she could not have supported the weight of the two of them. Swamped, she could take a man's weight in her still. But she could not carry the boy's weight as well.

The only way she could have taken the weight of the two of them was if they had both gone over the side and held on to her gunwale.

A curragh could support three men like that. But such a procedure was impossible in the storm. The rending force of the water would have torn them away from the curragh. Or if they held on to her, it would have broken her up. The only thing to do was to throw the boy overboard and he had done this and had no qualms of conscience about it.

It was what any seaman would do.

There was no room for mercy on the sea and no room for the weak. To survive on the sea a man had to have no weaknesses. He had to be as strong and ruthless as the ocean itself. And he survived. He was the only one of all the men out in curraghs during the White Storm who had survived.

He remembered once talking to a man who had been on a ship during the war that had been torpedoed. He had found part of a raft in the water—one of the kind of rafts they used to stack up on the decks of the ships in wartime in case of torpedoing. There wasn't much of it but there was enough to support him. On the raft, embedded in the side of it, flung there by some freak of the explosion, was a baling hook—a wicked steel hook for lifting sacks and other soft but cumbersome cargo with.

"The baling hook saved me," the man told him. "Mind you the bit of raft could support me and me only. There were others trying to get to it. I gave them the choice of swimming away or using the baling hook on them. They cursed me and pleaded with me and some drowned a few yards off. But they didn't come on my bit of raft and so I was saved.

"Sorry for it? Not me. I'm alive, ain't I? And they're all dead. It was my bit of luck to find that baling hook and I made good use of it."

No. He had no qualms about throwing the boy overboard. He wouldn't be alive himself if he hadn't. But now he was uneasy. There was a reckoning to be paid and the stranger was connected with the reckoning.

He decided he would go and see Caitlin the Other House. She was the one who had first seen the stranger and might know something about him. He took a pollack he had caught and went to her house, knowing she would welcome the gift.

"I have a fish for you," he said when she had opened the door of the cottage to him.

"It is a welcome gift," she replied. "But do you think that one fish will ease your mind, Tom Joyce?"

"There is nothing on my mind to be eased," he replied.

"You did not walk from the village with a fish for me, to pass the time of day," replied Caitlin. "But sit down and I will make a mouthful of tea for you and then you can tell me what you want."

She had her back to him, bending over the hearth and busying herself with a kettle of hot water and a teapot. But now she turned around and stood erect and looked at him. She seemed tall and slender and he saw immediately the change in her. The bones of her face were touched by the light from the turf fire and there was about her face a beauty he had never seen before. It did not look old any longer but serene and youthful.

"The years have dropped from you, Caitlin the Other House," he said. "There is the look of April about you."

"It is the doing of the stranger," she said. "It was he who moved the blood in my heart and gave me back my youth. It is a heavy burden to carry a dead heart through the world for sixty years." She looked at him shrewdly. "You would know something of that, since the storm," she added.

"I do not know what you are talking about," he said roughly, but he was afraid.

They sat for a while in silence listening to the sea sounds outside the cottage and the little rustlings of the wind against the thatch and the complaining noise the steam made as it trickled out of the spout of the kettle on the hearth.

Tom Joyce was sorry he had come to visit Caitlin the Other House now. She had the reputation of a witch in the village and he was afraid that far from helping him she might now do him some harm, for she seemed to have divined, very readily, his secret, which up to that time, he believed, was known to no one in Killknock.

He felt that she knew not only what lay in his past but also what lay in his future and that she could control this according to her own desires. But he was afraid that she did not wish him well and rather than say anything that might give her offense, he determined to be silent and leave all the talking to her.

After a while she spoke, holding her teacup before her in both hands and looking to the glowing fire as if she were talking to it rather than to him.

"Ireland is a place that does not change except in the surface things, and even these are only a disguise for the things that have not changed and that lie beneath them. It is a place that lies on the very edge of the world and there is nothing to the west of it except America and that is part of the new world and has nothing to do with the world that was here before America was ever discovered.

"All the old gods and all the old peoples were driven across Europe and this was the last place in the world that they could go to. Beyond Ireland there was only the ocean and so they stayed here at the end of the world. And they are here to this day.

"The people of England think that they are an old people and so do the people of Gaul. But they are a people new to their land, for they have hardly been on it two thousand years and that is no time at all.

"But we here in Ireland are the oldest people in Europe living on their own soil. For if you were to go back five thousand years, you would find in Ireland the same kind of people who are living in it today.

"We in Ireland are the last of the Celts and there is more in our story than in the stories of all the countries of Europe though little of it is known and less written down. Have you ever thought of that, Tom Joyce: how old we are, you and I?"

"I have never thought of it," he said. "I am as old as I am, which is from the day I was born to the moment that I speak in now."

"You are older than that by thousands of years," replied Caitlin of the Other House in a soft voice. "For we are a people who were never separated from our folklore nor our island nor our old gods. They are around you, Tom Joyce, and they are in your blood and if you had a son or a daughter, they would be in his blood too. You are five thousand years old and even more than that. Do you know why you love the sea, why you spend your time in your curragh on the ocean though there is no profit from it?"

"It is because I love the sound of it and the sight of it," he said.

"It is because the sea is the life that is in you, Tom Joyce, and you and the sea are one. You are a sea creature. For you the ocean is no dead thing but a living force and even on the pleasantest day you look at it and feel the power that is in it and the threat that is in it. That was the way it was in the old times when men worshiped the sea."

"In the winter gales," said Tom Joyce, "the surf breaking on the headland shakes the village and I have felt it on the other side of the mountain. I have felt the mountain itself shake from the breaking of the waves. Once I went halfway up the mountain in a gale. The air was black with the wind and on the side of the mountain there was seaweed—the gowla weed which grows in great forests at the depth of fifteen fathoms. The sea had ripped it from the bottom and the wind had caught it and had thrown it against the side of the mountain."

"The Mountain of Mananaan," said Caitlin the Other House.

"Yes. The Mountain of Mananaan. It was an offering. The weed was as thick on the side of the mountain as it was on the beach and I caught one glimpse of the ocean at that time and then I could not look at it any more."

"What did you see?" the woman asked.

"It was like nothing any man has seen before or since," replied the fisherman. "It was all writhing and white from the headland to the horizon. It had raised itself up into the air so that it seemed that it must come over the land. There were streamers of spume from it that seemed a quarter of a mile long and some of them flew flat over the surface but some of them were twisted and snaked up toward the sky and then, in the instant that I saw them, were torn apart by the wind so that the ocean was above the ocean.

"The spray flung solid against the side of the mountain, which you know is three miles from the headland, and the noise from the ocean was like the crumbling of the world itself."

"And you were afraid?"

"I was afraid."

"And you are still afraid?"

"Someday the ocean will kill me," he said in a low voice. "Someday soon."

"And you brought me a fish thinking that I would tell you how to save yourself? Is that all your life is worth to you, Tom Joyce?"

"I had nothing else," he said.

"It is no matter," she said, "for there is nothing I can do to help you. You can only help yourself and if you will think, you will know what it is you must do."

At that they parted but Tom Joyce did not return to the village, for he wanted to be alone to sort out his thoughts. He was not a man of any agility of mind and not knowing where to turn for advice now that Caitlin of the Other House had failed him, he went across the bog and started climbing, without being aware of what he was doing, up the lower slopes of the mountain. When he had gone about a third of the way up, to the place where the turf finally petered out to be replaced by sharp little terraces of limestone in whose crevices grew the strange plants which drew botanists to Killknock from many parts of the world, he decided that he would climb to the top of the mountain.

The exercise might take away some of the heaviness of his mind and from the top he could get a view of the ocean and this panorama was something worth seeing. Before he left the area of the turf, however, he found a piece of sally grass and a piece of heather and then going to a small stream which was one of many that rippled down the mountain side, he searched in it until he found a round pebble.

He needed these because of the stones on the top which would have to be appeased if he was to come safely down from the mountain again. With them he continued to climb, not looking toward the peak, but keeping his eyes on the ground a few feet in front of him. It was easier to climb that way because he was not then discouraged by the distance which still had to be gone nor the height which had to be reached.

After a while he stopped and still not looking at the peak, sat down and looked across the boglands to the mountain on the other side. He was about on the same level as they, for Knockmor was the highest of all the mountains about.

He could see the peak behind the O'Flaherty cottage and he noticed that the two bullans, the Man of Stone and the Woman of Stone, were no longer standing on the top.

They could not be seen at all.

He was immediately frightened, for there was only one explanation that came immediately to his mind. And that was that the stones were thirsty and were starting on their way down the mountain to drink in the Lake of the Stones.

He had his back to the peak of Knockmor and he dared not look around, for he feared that the stones on the top would likewise be missing and would be on their way down also to the lake. If he saw them moving he could himself be turned into a stone. And then he heard a slight noise above him and the flesh crawled on him with fright, for he thought the stones were certainly on their way to the lake.

A shadow came over him and he was immediately cold, and to his right and a little below him a sea hawk whirled suddenly over the shoulder of the mountain screaming in fury. Then the noise he had heard ceased and there was a deep silence on the mountain.

He turned around and saw the stranger standing near the peak. He got up quickly and scrambled upward toward the stranger. A rag of mist floated between them and when it had gone it was not the stranger who was standing there but the Stone of Mananaan.

It had at the top and in its center a circle carved and the circle was filled with lines which whirled outward toward the circumference. There were a number of wavy lines below the circle. At the foot of the stone was a flat boulder, like a primitive altar.

There was a depression in the middle of this. In olden times it was filled with the blood of sacrifices to the god.

But there had been no blood in it for many centuries and it seemed, to the fisherman, dust-dry and thirsty.

Chapter Eight

RINCEY the cobbler never knew such peace in all his days as when the stranger came to stay with him. There was something about the man that smoothed away all cares and disturbances of the mind; all the little frettings that erode away a man's spirit and make his day, from rising to retiring, slightly troubled and nervous. Rincey had many of these minor anxieties.

He owed seventy-five shillings for leather to a merchant in Galway and the money was due to be paid in two weeks but he had not been able to get it together. Or rather, when he got it together, he spent it, shilling by shilling, on little extras for himself or for Mairin.

And so now he had only forty-nine shillings saved and the merchant was not the kind of a man who would take a part of payment. There would be no more leather until the full sum was forthcoming. And his own stock of leather was low.

That was one thing to fret about.

Then there was the damp under his workbench. He worked in front of a window facing the street with a view over it of the harbor wall. The floor of his workroom was rough-paved with limestone flags. But the damp came through and recently came through very heavily. His feet then were always cold and though he put a sack on the floor for his feet, the damp got through that. The solution, he had been told, was to have the floor cemented, for it was plain that there was a little spring under the floor. But cementing cost money and he had none. Every day when he opened his workroom he saw the dark damp area about which he could do nothing and it vexed him for the rest of the day.

Also he had a cleddin.

It was perfectly natural to have a cleddin. All cobblers got cleddins. It was the result of having to sit hunched up for so long. The lungs became restricted and the chest bones gradually slipped out of place and constricted the lungs further. So he had difficulty breathing and had a pain in his side which troubled him during his work and interrupted his sleep.

And then there was the man he had shot, long long

ago—the man who had pleaded to be allowed to live and had been saying something about his wife and his children when Rincey had squeezed the trigger of his revolver and it had jerked a little in his hand and the bullet had smashed into the man's red forehead and he had gone down to his knees and then fallen on his face on the road.

Rincey tried not to think of this. Sometimes he succeeded for periods of days in avoiding the thought. But finally the whole scene would come vividly before him and he would groan aloud and say, "No. No," as if to undo what he had done by the agony of his spirit. But it was no use. The man was dead. Rincey prayed often for him. He prayed that his soul would soon be released from Purgatory to Heaven. And then he prayed for forgiveness for killing him without even giving him a chance to make his peace with God.

But after the stranger came to stay with him, these troubles were soothed away for Rincey. The stranger was very gentle and kind. His manner was soft and his smile was warm and so was his presence. He brought a great rest to Rincey and the second day the stranger was with him, the cobbler decided that whatever his business he could not be a gunman. No gunman, no killer, could have that effect on anybody. Furthermore the donkey liked him. Donkeys were beasts specially blessed by God who had ridden on the back of one of them many a time. And a donkey would not like a man of blood.

Rincey did not see the stranger in the mornings—

only in the evenings. He had to get up very early and go out on his little farm at the foot of the mountain and bring his two cows to a shed which stood in his field, to be milked. Then he brought the milk home and made his breakfast. Then he went to his work in his workshop. The stranger slept all this time. Mairin made his breakfast for him and then he would be off with the girl, spending the greater part of the day with her.

Sometimes they went to the beach together and sometimes they went exploring over the bogs. They came back for dinner and that was the meal they all three had together. Rincey made it. There wasn't much variety to it—either some boiled bacon and cabbage and potatoes, or some boiled mutton and cabbage and potatoes. And of course soda bread which the cobbler made, for he was handy in the kitchen, having lived so long without a woman in his house.

At dinner then, he would be with the stranger and Mairin would talk about what they had done that day. Her talk was full of fancies.

"When you get high up in the air," she said, "you can see the wind."

"Is that so now?" said Rincey.

"It is," said Mairin. "You can see it on the grass and on the trees for it turns them to a silver and you can see it on the lakes and the ocean for it makes them dark. Sometimes the wind is blowing one way and then not very much higher up it is blowing the other way. It is like two big rivers one on top of the other and each going in a different direction. When birds like geese and swans are going to fly a long way, they pick one of these rivers of wind going in their direction and they go with it. It is like swimming downstream for them. They can go thousands of miles that way."

"And how do you know that?" asked the cobbler.

"Because I was up in the wind with the geese this morning," said Mairin. "We did not go very far, only to Derry and back again."

"That is a hundred miles if it is a hundred yards," said her father smiling.

"It is not far when you travel with the wind," said the girl. Rincey looked at the stranger to excuse the girl's fancies, but there was no need for the look, for the stranger was smiling.

"Everybody thinks ice is white with black parts to it where the light doesn't catch it right," continued the girl. "But it isn't white at all. Sometimes it is as green as a glass bottle and sometimes it is as blue as the sky and sometimes it is so red you can hardly look at it because it's like looking into a fire. I mean the red is all sparkling and hurts your eyes. And up in the north, far far away, there are great big mountains of ice that are the colors of all the jewels in the world. Some of them have holes right through them and the deeper you go into the hole the greener it gets."

"And how would you know that?" asked Rincey.

"Wasn't I there myself just the other day," replied Mairin.

"You've a great mind for fancies," said the cobbler, "and I will tell you one thing that is true. If you are able to fancy a place, why it is just the same as being there or even much better.

"When I was a boy I fancied myself many a time in Africa and if I were to be taken to Zanzibar this moment, there isn't a thing about it that would surprise me. I've seen it all before, you see. Yes, and smelled it too, for Zanzibar is a place that has a wonderful smell to it. There's the smell of the stuff they call copra, you see, that is dried coconuts. And the smell of dried fish and with it the smell of spices like tamarinds and nutmegs and suchlike. And there's a stall there that is stacked high with ivory and an Arab with one eye that sells the poor heathen blacks into slavery. And there's an elephant comes down the streets of Zanzibar with gold on its tusks and silver rings as heavy as a blacksmith's anvil on its feet and a sultan on its back looking like a peacock for the jewels that are on him. It's a wonderful thing to have a powerful fancy, for the whole world is yours whenever you care to roam around in it.

"Did you have such fancies when you were a boy, sir?"

"I did indeed," said the stranger. "I would take chips of wood and think they were Roman galleys sailing to Egypt."

99

"May I go to Zanzibar tomorrow and see the elephant with the silver on his feet?" asked the girl of the stranger.

"That might be a mistake," replied the stranger gravely. "When you go there you might not find the elephant and that would be a disappointment."

"If you said I would find him I would," said Mairin. "But perhaps it would be better to go somewhere else instead."

"You can go anywhere your fancy takes you," said Rincey. "And that is the truth of it."

To treat the pain in his side, the cleddin, Rincey did not go to Dr. McEwan. First of all he tried to ignore it and some days it did not trouble him very much. He thought it would go away, particularly if he spent a while after work each day straightening his chest and standing up without stooping and taking a breath or two of air at the window of his room which was directly over his shop.

But the pain persisted.

The principal reason he did not go to Dr. McEwan about it was because he was afraid the doctor would send him into the hospital in Galway for an examination. That was what usually happened. That would mean days in the hospital and perhaps weeks and he would be without Mairin except when she could come to visit him, which would not be often.

Furthermore, once you got into a hospital it was very hard to get out again. You could say that you were well until you were blue in the face but nobody there would believe you. You only got out when the people in the hospital agreed that you were well and that might be a very long time. He could not bear to be a long time away from Mairin and furthermore if he went to the hospital, she would be frightened.

In Killknock people only went to the hospital in Galway to die. That was a well-known thing. Everybody who ever went to the hospital from the village died there. Dr. McEwan said that that was because they did not go in time. But who would go early to the place they were going to die in?

So instead of going to Dr. McEwan, Rincey went to a folk doctor who lived over in Inishlacken and whose name was known to the villagers though Dr. McEwan didn't know anything about her. The folk doctor was a woman, Mrs. Coleman.

Her husband was dead thirty years and she had a little cottage on the island and four fields and two cows. She had no children. But though she was close to seventy she ran her farm herself and could doctor animals as well as men and women.

She was a great hand with horses, and the only one who could cure the haws in a horse. If a horse were left out in the cold weather it likely would get the haws.

A wart developed overnight in one of its eyes and the horse would stand with its hind legs straddled and could walk only haltingly. If the owner brought the horse to

Mrs. Coleman (it had to be done secretly) she would sew the eyelid together to stop the horse blinking and then cut out the wart. To do this the horse's head had to be put through a window or some such aperture so the horse could be handled the better and two men held it there, one holding its upper lip and another its lower.

As soon as the wart was cut out, the horse was well. She could also reset a dislocated shoulder in a horse or a cow by making cuts in the hide over the dislocation and threading a stick through them in a certain way and then bandaging the place for a couple of days. The dislocation was mended fast by this method and no harm done to the horse or cow but a few cuts on its skin that would soon heal up.

Mrs. Coleman also could treat the cleddin. And so one day shortly after the stranger had arrived, Rincey went over to Inishlacken to see Mrs. Coleman, taking five shillings with him which he thought would likely be her fee.

"I have a catch in my side and I think it is a cleddin from stooping over all day mending shoes and my feet damp all the time," he said when they had exchanged greetings.

"Rest yourself and have a cup of tea and we will see what can be done about it," said Mrs. Coleman. "You would not have thought to bring a little tobacco with you, coming over from the mainland."

"I did indeed," said Rincey. "I have a plug of Yachtsman here I brought thinking you might welcome it."

"When I was a girl I would have thrown it in your face, Rincey the Cobbler," said Mrs. Coleman. "But now I am an old woman and welcome it. Isn't it strange the way things turn out now? When I was a young girl it was a silk shawl from Spain I had my heart on. One I could wear to the church and have the women boiling with envy. And now I'd take a plug of tobacco before the best shawl that was ever made. When you are young you want to be a queen in the world. But when you are old, comfort is all you care about."

He gave her the plug of tobacco, wrapped in its tin-foil sheath, and she reached to the mantel and took down a clay pipe with but two inches of stem. The part of the stem that went in her mouth was sucked as clean as a bone but the rest of it and the bowl as well was as black as a coal. She undid the wrapping of the plug of tobacco with hands so knobbly and distorted that they looked to Rincey like a worn-out pair of shoes. She cut a piece off the plug with a knife that she first of all sharpened with three slashes on the stone of the hearth, and rubbed the tobacco out and put it in the pipe. Then she reached down to the fire and picked up a piece of burning turf and with this lit her pipe.

There was a pot of oatmeal cooking on the hearth and Rincey looked at it for a moment and thought that it was strange that oatmeal should be cooking in the middle of the afternoon.

"It's the cow," she said, seeing his look. "She will drop her calf tonight with the tide. She is a mean mother. I can tell you that. In the pain she will hate the calfeen and will not clean it up nor let it suckle. But I will put the oatmeal on the calf and she will lick it for the smell. And then she will forget her pain and anger and clean the calf and let it get to her teats."

"It is well known that a calf born in the flood tide will be strong," said Rincey.

"A calf and a child," said Mrs. Coleman. "And those that come with the ebb of the tide are sickly all their days."

She took her pipe out of her mouth long enough to take a suck of the tea from the big delft cup on the table before her. She held the tea for some time in her mouth, rolling it around to savor the strength of it and the sugar, and then swallowed it. If I said she was ugly, said Rincey to himself, I wouldn't be giving half the truth of it. There were three hairs on the end of her nose and they were white and stiff and ugly to see growing out of the deadish-looking flesh. She wore a shawl all the time, in and out of her house, and no one had seen her with it off.

"There is a stranger in your house," the woman said at length, "and I hear that he is a great healer, for from the time Feeney set eyes on him he is not deaf any more. Is that the truth?"

"It is," said Rincey. "But Dr. McEwan says that it is just a kind of a change inside Feeney's ear that could have happened at any time and it was only chance that it happened when the stranger came in."

"Dr. McEwan," said Mrs. Coleman in scorn. "He has got a diploma from a college in Dublin to show that he knows a few things about healing and is ignorant of all the rest. I'll tell you what is the matter with those doctors from the colleges. They forget that the power of healing is in the hands and they think that it is in bottles. But you cannot heal anyone without having the power in your hands and all the studying that was ever done will not give it to you unless you come by it naturally."

"That's the truth," said Rincey, partly because he believed this to be so but more because he thought it better to agree with her.

"Tell me, did this stranger touch Feeney in any way to cure him of his deafness?"

"He did not. He came in and spoke and Feeney heard what was being said from that moment on."

"Then he must be a very great healer indeed," said Mrs. Coleman. "My love to him that he came to this part of the world. I wonder you did not ask him to cure you of the cleddin, and he in your house."

"But I did not know that he is a healer at all," said Rincey. "And I would be timid to ask him the favor anyway, for he is my guest and it is not right to ask a favor of a guest."

"There is some truth in that," said Mrs. Coleman. "Well, you must take off your shirt and lie on the table there and I will get the cleddin out of you."

Rincey did as bid and she positioned him on the table so that his head and shoulders were hanging over the sides and he had to hold on to the edges of the table not to fall on the floor.

In this position with the upper part of his torso hanging from the table, Mrs. Coleman leaned over him and put the heels of her distorted hands under his rib cage and telling him to hold to the table as hard as he might, pushed with all the force she could muster. The effect was to lift the ribs upward and bend the spine, or rather that portion of the spine which was not supported by the table, backward. Despite her age she had great strength and Rincey could feel the whole rib cage and the bones of his shoulders being pushed upward and backward.

For a moment or two the sensation was pleasant but then he experienced severe pain from the punishment of his skin and muscles under the pushing of the woman. His pursed lips parted from the pain and a dew of sweat broke out on his temples but he said nothing. After a while Mrs. Coleman relaxed. But it was only to repeat the performance again, and not just once but three times, so that Rincey felt she would push the ribs out of him through his shoulders before she was done.

He felt a few minor clicks in his skeleton and concluded that the bones which had come out of place restricting the lungs and causing the cleddin were now in their normal position.

But this was not the end of the treatment. For when it was done she had him lie upon the floor with his face on his arms and his head turned to the side. And then she put her foot upon his spine and put all her weight upon it in several places and now he could really feel the bones clicking.

"You're straightened out now, Rincey," said Mrs. Coleman when she was done, "but I will tell you that your skeleton was in a pitiful condition. It is a wonder you could draw a breath at all. Tell me, do you feel any ease?"

"I do indeed," said Rincey and certainly it was true, for the pain in his side had gone and it seemed to him that he was capable, for the first time in several months, of getting a good lungful of air.

"Well there will be poisons in you that will have to be taken out too," said Mrs. Coleman. "And for that you will have to use suckage. You'll know about that, I suppose."

"I do not," said Rincey.

"Well it is an easy thing," said Mrs. Coleman. "When you go to bed at night take a little empty glass and put it on your stomach above the navel and leave it there for a little while. You will find that the flesh will creep up inside the glass and when it does that, it is because the poisons are being drawn out of you. Do that now three or four days. Every day you do it, there will be less of the flesh pulled up into the glass. And when the day comes that your skin is not pulled up by the glass at all, then you are clear of the poisons.

"Tell me," she continued, "and how is Mairin? I have not seen her since the day she was born."

"She is well and it's a great thing for her that the stranger has come and is staying in the house. For he takes her everywhere but her head is so full of fancies that she talks of flying through the air with the geese and such things as that."

"Is it the geese or with swans?" asked Mrs. Coleman.

"Geese," said Rincey.

"Well, there's no harm in that at all. But if it were swans I would be uneasy for the child, for swans are fond of human company and there is many a child missing in Ireland that was taken away by the swans. A child near swans is always in danger and I would advise you to keep her away from them. There is a black swan that has come to Inishlacken two days ago. It flew over the island from the south to the north and I can tell you the women got their children into their houses fast enough when they saw it. Did you see the black swan in Killknock at all?"

"I never heard of it," said Rincey.

"It put a great fright on everybody on the island including the animals. It had a red beak and little golden eyes and it flew in the direction of Knockmaan. Is there any news from the mainland at all that you could tell me?"

"There is a great change has come over Caitlin the Other House since the stranger came. If I said to you that she had dropped forty years from her life, and those the heavy ones, you would understand what I mean. She was the first one in the village to meet him and from the time of their meeting she has lost all her cares and is like a young girl on a spring day with the wind soft from the south."

"Now there is wonder in that," said Mrs. Coleman. "And Feeney they say has not had a deaf moment since he came."

"It is the truth."

"And yourself that sees him every day. How does he strike you?"

"I have had great peace of mind since he has been in my house, for all my little cares have gone and only the big ones remain."

"So everyone in the village likes him?"

"Not everyone," said Rincey. "I do not know the reason but Tom Joyce is afraid of him."

"Why would that be?" asked Mrs. Coleman but she asked the question as if she knew the answer herself and suspected that Rincey knew also.

"I do not know," said Rincey. "He has not spoken to me about it nor to anyone else. He was always a person that kept to himself. But there was another strange thing that happened since the stranger came to the village. The Man of Stone and the Woman of Stone on the mountain behind the O'Flaherty cottage have fallen forward on their faces and the talk is that they will soon go to the lake with all the other stones from atop Knockmaan to drink in the lake."

"And this happened when the stranger came?" asked Mrs. Coleman.

"The night before. It happened during the night and Caitlin the Other House met the stranger on the hot road the very next day. But I do not believe the story of the stones myself. It is all foolishness from the old days."

"You do not believe it now, Rincey the Cobbler, while you are sitting safe in this house in Inishlacken. But would you go to the Lake of Stones tonight or any other night and stay there a while?"

"I would not," said Rincey.

"Then do not tell me that you do not believe that the stones drink in the lake or have power over the people in the village," said Mrs. Coleman.

It was time for Rincey to get going now. He had rowed over to Inishlacken himself, having borrowed a curragh from Tom Joyce, and he wanted to get back again before dark.

So he thanked the woman for her help and put five shillings on the table, for there was a vestige of aristocracy among the people and they did not like to take money directly from each other for services rendered.

Mrs. Coleman stood at the door of her cottage watching the little cobbler go down the boreen to the harbor where the curragh was.

"I have put a little hope into you," she said to herself, watching him go, "and you have given me five shillings. But you will not live to see the next year, for it is the *aisle* that has a grip on you and there is no cure for that but death."

She watched while the curragh pulled out on the ocean for the mainland. The sea was a pale green and so calm that the fluffy clouds in the sky were mirrored on its surface. The bow wave of the curragh spread out in two delicate lines from the boat. All was peaceful in the little fields and upon the ocean and so quiet that if a stone had been dropped anywhere in the world, it would have been distinctly heard on the island.

It was, indeed, as quiet as death.

Chapter Nine

D R. McEWAN was not an athletic kind of man but every now and then he was overtaken by a desire for strenuous exercise as some people are overtaken by a desire to get drunk and others by fits of sanctity. Father Dimmock said that this was because he was from the Six Counties and torn therefore physically, spiritually and mentally between Ireland and England, between Gael and Saxon.

"The Irish," the priest said, "are allergic to mere exercise for the health of the body. You will never hear of an Irishman going for a walk just to be walking. If he goes for a walk at all it is to poach a salmon or a hare or to visit someone he wants to sit down and talk to. In general the Irish will do nothing that requires labor unless convinced that it is necessary.

"But the English cannot leave undone those things that do not require doing at all. They are forever puttering around trying to find something to do, for it is extremely painful for them not to have their bodies occupied. This makes it necessary for them to amuse themselves with their minds and, God forgive them, they lack the equipment.

"So an Englishman is always working at something or another and when he has no labor to occupy himself with, he takes a walk for the good of his health. You would not get an Englishman to climb barefoot to the top of a mountain, as is done every year on Croagh Patrick, to worship God. When he climbs a mountain it is purely for his physical health, and there is the difference between the two countries and the two people—the Irish are a spiritual people and the English are a physical people.

"And you, Doctor, are torn between the two. You have enough Celt in you to avoid unnecessary physical labor for several weeks. And then you are overcome with remorse and out you go on a long walk, sucking in the fresh air and blistering your feet, all in the belief that it will improve your character."

"Bah," snorted Dr. McEwan. "The only real vigor there is in the whole of Ireland is in the Six Counties and the rest of the country is speeding headlong—"

"To Heaven," interrupted the priest with a smile. "Why don't you join us?"

"I am going to climb to the top of Knockmor," said the doctor.

"For your health, I suppose," said the priest. "And carrying the whole British Empire on your shoulders."

Dr. McEwan could not think of a reply on the moment and having instructed his assistant to make a note of callers, but in no circumstance to prescribe anything for them, off he went.

He stopped in first at Feeney's bar to see whether the man still had his hearing. Feeney had not been born deaf. The deafness had come on him during his youth and the doctor attributed it to the growth of a lesion in the inner ear. It was not unusual for such lesions to disappear so that hearing was restored and he believed that this was what had happened in Feeney's case. The point was whether the lesion would return again.

"Good day," he said as soon as he was in the little bar.

"Good day to you, sir," said Feeney. "What would be your pleasure?"

"I won't take anything," said the doctor. "How is your hearing?"

" 'Tis like a fox," said Feeney. "I believe I could hear two blades of grass rubbing against each other in the wind or a fly landing on a pound of butter in the front shop or the little hiss the sun makes when it dips down into the ocean in the evening, and, as you know yourself, sir, 'tis only children that can hear that at all."

"By God I don't know about your hearing but there is nothing the matter with your tongue, Feeney," replied the doctor and at that Tim Conneeley, who was in the bar, put back his turnip-shaped head with the dirty caubin on it and gave a big shout of laughter. Then he solemnly placed his half-empty glass of Guinness on the little shelf that ran around the room and looked at it as if there was a great deal of wisdom in what he had done.

" 'Twas the stranger that cured him," he said. "The stranger and none other." And he picked up his glass again as if to show that he had said the first and the last and the only word worth saying in the matter.

"Damned nonsense," snorted Dr. McEwan. "There was a lesion in Feeney's ear and, if he would be honest about it, he would admit that his hearing had been improving for several days. The final improvement—the falling away of the last remnants of the lesion—coincided with the arrival of this stranger. If it was a duck that walked into the bar at the moment, the lot of you would be saying that he was cured by a duck."

"We would not say that at all," said Tim Conneeley, "for any man of sense knows that a duck can cure nothing. *You* might say that he had been cured by a duck, but *we* would not say it."

"And what would you say?" demanded the doctor.

"We would say that he had been cured by one of the

shee that had taken the form of a duck," said Tim Conneeley with great composure and an appearance of sense. "An ordinary duck could do nothing."

"God help you in your ignorance and superstition," said the doctor.

"The stranger is a great healer," said Tim Conneeley. "If you were to give him a list of all the people that are sick in the village, and asked him to cure the lot, you wouldn't have a stroke of work to do for the rest of the year."

"Does he say he is a great healer?" bristled the doctor, sensing a chance to make a complaint against the stranger although he had never met him. Still, a doctor does not like someone completely unskilled giving himself a reputation of a healer in his practice.

"He does not," said Tim Conneeley, "and there is no need for him to do so, for it is something that everybody knows. I think he could cure Rincey the cobbler of the cleddin if he had a mind to do it or if Rincey would ask him. But he's too timid."

"Has Rincey got a cleddin?" asked the doctor quickly. Rincey had never been to see him, but he knew about cleddins. They were either lung cancer or tuberculosis and whenever he heard of a case he sent the man into the hospital in Galway for examination. This, of course, was the reason he rarely heard of the complaint, for no one in Killknock liked to go to the hospital which was a place, as remarked before, where people went to die.

Tim Conneeley exchanged a look of pure misery with Feeney. He had said the wrong thing. He had a desire to be taken for a wise and sober man, one in whom confidence could be placed without anxiety. But it was his fate to be constantly saying the wrong thing, to be betraying confidences and little secrets not through any maliciousness but through a kind of clumsiness of mind.

"It isn't what I would exactly call a cleddin," he said to the doctor. "No. A cleddin is not the name I would put to it at all."

"Come on," said the doctor in his abrupt Six Counties manner. "Have it out. What is the matter with Rincey?"

"I hear tell he has a little pain in his side," said Tim Conneeley.

"It's nothing more than wind," said Feeney leaning across the bar and looking earnestly at the doctor. "Nothing more than wind, I'd say. You can take it from me."

"And in any case it will trouble him no more," said Tim Conneeley, "for he was off to see—" He was about to blurt out the fact that Rincey had been to see Mrs. Coleman on Inishlacken but Feeney saved him by the expedient of dropping a pint glass on the rough cement floor. It shattered with a sharp explosion followed by a tinkle as the fragments scattered over the concrete against the wall. Feeney beamed at the doctor.

"Now there's something for your medical books," he said. "There's a world of pleasure in listening to the shattering of a glass for a man that has been deaf for thirty years. I suppose you don't listen to it yourself with any pleasure, for I noticed that when I dropped the glass you winced and shut your eyes. But if you would listen to it carefully you would find that it is a delightful experience and it isn't one noise at all but three separate kinds of noises and each one of them is a darling on its own.

"First of all, do you see, there is a kind of a thump when the glass hits the floor. It's like giving a good bang to a drum, for it has a hollow kind of sound to it. And then there is a sharp crack that is like ten dry sticks being broken. It's a nice clean sound, as neat, I would say, as the paw of a fox. And after that there is the little tinkle sound like bells when the pieces of glass dance over the concrete. And all that, mind you, to be had from dropping a pint measure on the floor of the bar. I'll tell you something, Doctor. Since the stranger gave me back my hearing, I've dropped one a day, just for the pleasure of the sound it makes when it goes to pieces."

He moved a glass over to the doctor. "You wouldn't like to try one yourself, I suppose," he said.

"I would not," said Dr. McEwan. Feeney, with his description of the breaking of a glass, had befuddled him momentarily. This was something that often happened to him in the Republic. Just when he was bringing the conversation to a sharp point out of which he could extract a hard core of sense, the others present would wrap it around, as it were, with a wool of words on some subject entrancing but quite remote from the topic in hand. And the point was lost. The priest was as adept at it as the rest of the villagers.

"Tell Rincey when you see him," he said, "that I want him up at the dispensary tomorrow. And if he doesn't come I'll send the sergeant for him."

"I seem to have heard a word passed that Rincey is going into Galway tomorrow," said Feeney.

"Well there is another word being passed that he is to come and see me instead," said the doctor and stormed out, as ruffled as he had been after discussing climbing the mountain with the priest.

When he had gone, Tim Conneeley turned to Feeney. "You're a good man, Feeney," he said. "You saved me from saying that Rincey had gone to see Mrs. Coleman in Inishlacken. I've a mind to do something to thank you."

He picked up his glass which was now empty and dropped it solemnly on the floor. The two of them listened to it shatter with delight.

Dr. McEwan could have taken a little lane which ran along the side of Feeney's bar to gain the flank of the mountain. It led through a couple of fields and then petered out into a sheep track on the fringe of the mountain and was the quickest way of getting to Knockmaan other than going up the village and around past the church. But he decided instead to walk out past the cottage in which Caitlin the Other House lived, for he had heard that this solitary woman, always so stern and sour, had undergone what, in psychiatric medicine, was called a "personality change" and looked and acted like a young woman.

This was also attributed to the stranger. He had read of cases in the British *Medical Journal* in which elderly women had achieved a measure of rejuvenation, usually as the result of hypnotic treatment. But the rejuvenation was only temporary, and they had quickly returned to their former age. It was just possible that the stranger was capable of inducing a temporary hypnosis. He wanted to find out.

Caitlin the Other House was leaning against the wall of the garden before her cottage when he met her, and though he was prepared for some signs of change in her, he was surprised at the freshness and the color of her skin and the brightness of her eyes. Indeed it seemed that she had filled out and become very much younger and he was so taken aback on seeing this that for a moment he could find nothing to say to her.

"I see you are looking very well," he said eventually when he had recovered a measure of his wits.

"I thank you for saying it, but it is nothing less than the truth," said the woman. "And to save you your next question I will tell you that it is the stranger that has brought about this change in me."

"Indeed," said the doctor, "and how is it that he has been able to do that?"

"Who am I to explain the power that lies in the stranger?" said Caitlin the Other House. "Is there anyone in the world who can explain one person to another person? I'll tell you all that can be done. You can explain about another person only those things that you find in yourself. And any strange thing in another person you cannot explain at all but only wonder at. And the stranger is like no man that has ever trod the world before—except perhaps one man."

"And who might that one man be?" asked the doctor.

"If I told you you would not believe me," said the woman. "But if you were to think about it and inquire around and study the stranger, then you would know for yourself."

Confound these Irish, said the doctor to himself. They'll never tell you anything plainly but wrap it all up in words as if words were meant to hide rather than to convey sense. And yet he knew that there was a sense in what Caitlin the Other House was telling him which was beyond his conception, and this added to his irritation.

He returned doggedly to his questioning. "Is there any one thing the stranger did that has brought about this change in you?" he asked.

But she did not reply to this directly. She looked past him to the distances of the bog with the mountains beyond—all dark green and bright gold, with the silver spears of water between—and the blue mountains against the horizon and the dark forms of the cloud sliding silently over the quiet spaces of the bogs over which the wind moved disturbing the grasses but making no sound.

"A barren woman is like a strand that the ocean has never reached," she said. "There is no strength to her but only sadness and weariness all her life. Her breasts pain her at the sight of other women's children so all of her cries for her own man and his strength and her child by him. There is no fulfillment for her without a child of her own and for a barren woman life is not life but a time of waiting to be brought into life by producing her own fruit.

"Men do not understand this. A man without a child is still a man. But a woman without a child is only a promise of a woman and so I have lived my years as the promise of a woman, for I have had no man of my own."

She said all this without bitterness, but in a quiet voice, patient with a long endurance and acceptance of what had been her lot. The doctor had not thought her capable of such depths, nor had he himself ever been more than vaguely aware of those deep but secret yearnings of women to hold a child of their own in their arms.

"You think I am past childbearing?" Caitlin the Other House asked looking at the doctor mildly. He nodded.

"It may be so," she said. "That may be the will of God. And yet the stranger has promised me that I will have a child and I believe him."

The doctor did not know what to say to that. Many women of a certain age—of the age of Caitlin the Other

House—convinced themselves in their loneliness and desperation that they were pregnant. These false pregnancies actually produced physical changes in them. Their breasts filled and their wombs expanded and they looked younger. They had all the physiological symptoms of pregnancy. But it was like the flowering of a dying tree in autumn. There was no fruit and after that only sadness and shame. He felt he ought to soften this inevitable blow for her, for he was a kindly man and loved all the villagers though he could never feel himself a part of them because of his different background, with its hard Six Counties tincture of practicality.

"Do not put any faith in this stranger," he said. "You will only be deceiving yourself and when the truth comes it will be hard to bear. In all medicine there is no case of a woman of your age bearing a child. Even if you had a husband—" He stopped, blushing, and vexed at himself that for all his medical experience, he could not take a clinical view of things and accept that it was possible for Caitlin the Other House to have a lover.

She laughed. It was a young laugh, full of teasing and pleasure. She stooped and picked up a pebble and threw it into the road. "Will you look for a moment at that pebble," she said.

The doctor looked at it.

"And now look at the mountain there beyond. The pebble is what you know and the mountain beyond is all the things that you do not know about. I will have my

child soon. At the time of the walking of the stones, I will have it."

"At what?" asked the doctor.

"The time of the walking of the stones. They will come down to the lake soon to drink. They are thirsty and started already." She told him of the Man of Stone and the Woman of Stone that had already moved behind the O'Flaherty cabin upon the mountain side.

"When did that happen?" he asked, interested despite his incredulity.

"The night before I met the stranger," she said.

"And I suppose that he had something to do with it?"

She did not answer and he left her and striking across the bogland, skirted the lake at the foot of Knockmor and started the climb up the sides of the mountain. On this flank the approach to the peak was leisurely; the other side of the mountain, which faced the ocean, being more precipitous.

He climbed slowly, however, busy with his thoughts which were mostly concerned with the world in which the people of the village lived. There was no explaining that world in rational terms. It was a world both of the present and the past and the future, so that it might be said of them that they did not live in time but rather in eternity.

They were more conscious of eternity than they were of the passing of the hours and of the days. The clock of the months and of the seasons had little actuality for them. They lived by an ocean measure—a vast and unending stream of time flowing from the past from unmeasurable distances into the future into unmeasurable distances.

That was what was real for them and gave them their peculiar view of life. The hour of the day was nothing and the month of the year was nothing. Spiritually they were tuned to vaster measures so that their prehistory was part of their present and their future was inseparably welded to the dark and unwritten events of the ancient life of the island—the ancient gods and the ancient heroes.

From generation to generation these people changed no more than the mountains changed and that was because they were not subject to reason. They had a higher or rarer motivation of their own, a spiritual motivation which made the young among them very wise and the old among them as full of dreams as children.

All this angered and at the same time awed the doctor. He was not quite able to come to grips with it. It was like trying to grasp a handful of the cobwebs that floated in the autumn days over the boglands. They seemed as real and as hard as strands of silver. But when you reached for them and enclosed them in your fingers, you had nothing. They had gone. The village people said they were not cobwebs. They said they were the souls of children who had been denied birth, drifting palely and mournfully over the boglands. Wish-children, like the child Caitlin the Other House had wished for and dreamed about so long.

Busy with such thoughts as these, the doctor got to the top of the mountain before he realized it. He had been walking with his eyes fixed only a few paces before him, so his view had been limited to the rutted limestones of the mountain and those strange plans which grew so surprisingly out of the stones. There was the pink sundew with its horrid hairy stem and its flesh-pink cup shaped not unlike a crocus. But the kind of a crocus the devil might devise. It trapped flies, wrapping its petals fiercely around them and digesting them until all that was left was the membrane of the wings. These remained when the pink chalice opened again and were blown off by the wind—the mute evidence of terrible death.

There were small purple flowers which grew with big broad leaves around them. He did not know the name of these. The flowers were no bigger than the head of a match but contained a virulent poison. The leaves were noxious also and if touched produced an intense irritation of the skin which developed in a day or two into a running sore. He had treated one or two cases of this kind of infection and assumed that it was something like that produced by poison ivy or poison oak.

While he had been thinking, he had seen such things passing below his feet and suddenly he felt a cold wind about his head and looking up saw that he was at the peak and the ocean breeze, previously deflected by the bulk of the mountain, was streaming around him.

Once on the mountain top, a feeling of depression, not untinged with fear, settled on him. It came upon him in a moment and seeking a reason for it, he thought, at first, it was because on this peak he was so far away from his fellows, so isolated from the people in the village below, as if he were indeed in mid-air or space, far far from them.

The Stone of Mananaan glowered at him from its little mound a hundred feet away. It seemed to be watching him. The crude circle carved in its top was like the eye of Cyclops, staring into his very essence, and very evil.

Almost without wishing to do so he walked toward the stone. He went slowly until he was standing at the foot of it, before the little altarlike dais that lay there. He did not look up at the stone now but at the altar and then he shuddered.

Lying on the altar were three pennies, sticky with the blood of a gutted fish that lay over them, and he knew that Mananaan, to whom human sacrifices had once been made, was still worshipped in the village.

Chapter Ten

DR. McEWAN told Father Dimmock of the sacrificial offering of the pennies and the gutted fish at the foot of the Stone of Mananaan on the peak of the mountain, and the priest was filled with a tremendous rage.

When these rages overcame him he was like the sons of Zebedee who had demanded of Christ that he call down fire and brimstone on those villages in Palestine whose inhabitants had refused to listen to him or had treated him with contempt.

He wished that in some striking manner the wrath of God would be visited on the people of Killknock to punish them for their persisting superstition. He would have liked to have gone through the village knocking men's heads together (something of which he was capable, for he was a big man) and thundering at them that they were nothing but pagans despite all the saints from Patrick on who had spent their lives bringing a sense of God to the people of Ireland.

Every year the villagers gave credence to the story of the thirsty stones going down to the lake to drink and kept in their houses on that night, and this was something that no Christian should believe, for it was nothing but superstition. They would not approach any of the bullans without first getting the magic leaf of sally grass and the piece of gorse and the round pebble (which he knew was a fertility symbol), and this was also an unclean and superstitious attitude. They reverenced the stones which were the old idols and it was the stones that ruled his parish as much as he. Or so he felt in his rage.

So he decided upon a plan to deal with the matter once and for all. It was a plan which would have appealed to Saint Patrick, for he had himself adopted it. He would take the villagers to the top of the mountain as their priests and they would throw the stones down. They would topple them over so that they no longer stood there overlooking the village, constantly in the sight of the people. And that would be the end of their persisting superstitions concerning them.

When Father Dimmock had arrived at this decision,

he wanted to put the plan into action right away. He was impetuous by nature and hated waiting and thinking things over. But, new from the seminary, he was aware that perhaps he ought to proceed with caution and consult someone first.

The bishop was the obvious person to consult with. But Father Dimmock did not like to do this. Although the bishop was his superior and the person to whom he should turn at all times for guidance, and although he sincerely held the bishop in the greatest respect, it was nonetheless a fact that the bishop was a townsman and did not know the people of the mountain and ocean country as he did. So, he went down to the doctor's house to put the plan to him and obtain his reaction.

I'll just tell him what I am going to do and I don't give a hang what he says about it, I'll do it anyway, the priest said to himself. But at least I will have consulted with somebody. It's true he's a Protestant but the Lord, for reasons of His own, didn't give all the sense to the Catholics. He may have some better way of doing the thing. There should be some dynamite in it anyway— an explosion that would blow the stones to smithereens. Why didn't I think of that before? I'll dynamite the devil back into Hell and good riddance to him.

Having thought of the dynamite, the priest felt much better and was in quite a pleasant mood when he reached Dr. McEwan's house. The doctor was in the dispensary when he arrived and Rincey the cobbler was buttoning his waistcoat, plainly following some kind of examination.

"Are you not in good health, Mr. Rincey?" asked the priest solicitously, for he was very fond of the cobbler and his little daughter Mairin.

"It is only a little bit of a thing that I have wrong with me," said Rincey. "Just a touch of the cleddin and, as the doctor will tell you, I'm as good as the day I was born."

He looked pathetically at the doctor who snorted, took the priest by the arm, and, leaving Rincey to be on his way home, led Father Dimmock into his sitting room.

"Just what is Rincey's condition?" asked the priest, who knew that few came to the doctor unless there was something seriously wrong with them.

"How am I to know?" snarled the doctor. "All I can do is listen to his lungs, take his blood pressure and a few specimens and send them into Galway. He should be in the hospital for a thorough examination and if I were worthy of my diploma, by God, there's where I'd send him. But there's his daughter, Mairin, with no one to look after her and a love between the two of them that is so strong that if you took one away you would kill the other with loneliness.

"I'll tell you what's the matter with Rincey. He's dying. I've seen so much of this kind of thing that I can almost tell the symptoms just by looking at him."

"What is it?" asked the priest. "Tuberculosis?"

"No," said the doctor, "if it was that there might be some hope for him. It's cancer. Lung cancer. Mind you, that's not a diagnosis. It's just a medical guess. But that's what's the matter with him. And he's had this pain in his side for two years. So I'd say it was too far advanced for an operation."

"How long will he live?" asked the priest.

The doctor looked at him quietly for a while before he answered. "That's not a question for me," he said softly. "It's a question for his Maker."

"I will have to find someone to take care of Mairin when he's gone," said the priest. "He has no relatives. I could get the bishop to put her in the convent in Galway."

The doctor got up and looked out of the window, his back to the priest. It was evening and he could see the ocean dark and impassive beyond the sea wall. The sky was lighter than the ocean and silhouetted against it was the island of Inishlacken. It seemed to undulate on the water, as if floating on it. There was a legend about an island that appeared off the coast once in every seven years. It was populated by immortals and if anyone could land on it or throw a lighted torch on it, they would themselves become immortal and know nothing but happiness through all eternity. Several of the villagers had told him they had seen this island when out in their curraghs. It was Tir na-n Og; the Land of the

Ever Young. There were times when he believed them. Mairin was the kind of person who should go to Tir na-n Og, the Land of the Ever Young, and not to a convent as an orphan to be brought up by the nuns. There was something about the child, as if she did not really belong to this world.

"Well, you didn't come to see me about Rincey," he said, turning away from the window and the dreams that lay beyond it. "What's on your mind, Father?"

"I'm going to get the villagers together and throw over the Stone of Mananaan," said the priest. "I'm going to do it right away. I will do it tomorrow at the latest. I will not let the sun rise nor set on that pagan idol one day more."

"Well, if that's what you're going to do, why come and tell me about it?" asked the doctor. "You don't require my permission to make a fool of yourself."

"In what way would I be making a fool of myself?" demanded the priest, irritated yet in some measure pleased that he was meeting with some opposition, for he wanted an argument on the subject before going ahead with his project. It would ease his mind if he could convince himself that he had discussed it with someone first.

"Well, first of all, there is the matter of whether you can throw the Stone of Mananaan over at all—without calling in the public works department and several engineers. I fancy that you are not the first priest that decided that it should be thrown down because of its influence on the people. But I expect it weighs three or four tons and there is as much of the stone below the ground as above. You'd look a trifle silly if you went up there with the whole of the village and told them to topple the stone over in the name of God. And then discovered you couldn't do it."

"I hadn't thought of that," said the priest. "But we could get some dynamite out of the quarry and blow it down."

"You could," said the doctor. "And you'd have a thousand archaeologists and anthropologists damning your name to the end of time. There'd be questions in the Dail and a committee formed for the protection of ancient monuments against the onslaughts of the ignorant priests of the Church of Rome. And up in the Six Counties every Protestant minister that ever wore an orange favor would throw his cap in the air and rejoice at the thought that a Catholic priest in the Republic had to destroy a pagan idol because of the devotion shown by his parishioners toward it."

Father Dimmock groaned. Blunt man that he was, he had never even considered these repercussions to his plan. It infuriated him that he must take them into consideration. It was grossly unfair. Patrick had not had to deal with public opinion when he overthrew the horrid idol Cromm Cruaich. He had just smashed it and that was that.

"Well, what are we to do?" he demanded. "We cannot leave it standing. You know that yourself, man."

"We?" said the doctor. "Faith, this is a strange turn. I'm not only a Protestant but I'm a nonconformist and an Orangeman. And now I'm part of a plan to save the prestige of a Roman Catholic priest and the soul of his parishioners."

"It isn't a matter of my prestige at all and you know that very well, Dr. McEwan," roared Father Dimmock. "I'm a humble man and I'll break the head of anyone who says I'm not. And as far as you being a Protestant and a nonconformist, that is never anything I have thrown up in your face. You must fight your own conscience about that, and I will pray for you and do all I can to save your soul. But I don't suppose that the Protestant Church, conformist or nonconformist, looks upon the worship of idols with any more tolerance than the Catholic Church. And I'm appealing to you now as a Christian. The Stone of Mananaan must go and you and I must see to it."

The doctor got up and went to a sideboard that contained an astounding display of crockery. There were cut-glass decanters that dated from the days of Queen Anne cheek by jowl with cheap cups and saucers from Woolworth's. There was a Regency salver and a huge soup tureen of genuine Sheffield plate and beside it a stack of plates decorated with outrageous shamrocks and harps and made in Japan.

He opened the cupboard below the sideboard and took out a whiskey decanter of cut Waterford glass and two tumblers of the same craftsmanship and without a word poured a quantity of whiskey into the bottom of each glass. He gave one to the priest and seating himself in a huge leather chair whose springing had long collapsed (making the chair more comfortable), sat for a few minutes swilling the whiskey around in the bottom of the glass. After a while, when it had been warmed a little, he sniffed it with the delicacy of a gardener sniffing a prize bloom, sighed with satisfaction, and swallowed the whiskey with one gulp.

"The glory that was Greece," he said, "and the grandeur that was Rome are small consolations to the world compared with whiskey which was the unique gift of the Celts to humanity. When a man is in need of solace, he will get more help from whiskey than from a view of the finest marble ever carved by a Phidias."

"He will that," said the priest. "But I do not see that this helps us with the problem of the Stone of Mananaan."

"You're too bullheaded," said the doctor. "When you see a problem you want to charge straight at it. That is because you're Irish. We Scots, living on the same piece of land as the Saxons, used to be the same way. The last time we charged was at Drummossie Moor in 1746. It was a magnificent charge, but it wiped out the last of the clans. After that we learned to be more circumspect. We learned to examine problems from all sides and look deeper into them. One result was that we established the Bank of England, lending money to the English at high rates of interest."

"For the love of God," cried Father Dimmock, "will you stop dealing with things that have nothing to do with the matter in hand and concentrate on the problem of overturning the Stone of Mananaan."

"Whiskey's wasted on you," said the doctor sulkily and helped himself again from the decanter.

"All right," he said. "The Stone of Mananaan. But first of all, tell me. What good do you think it will do to throw it over?"

"What good will it do?" cried the priest. "Well, it will get rid of an object of scandalous superstition which has had a grip on the minds of the people of this parish from time immemorial."

"I doubt it," said the doctor. "These people here have a feeling for the supernatural that goes beyond stones and is the growth of thousands of years. They live closer to the supernatural than people in other parts of the world. Maybe it has something to do with the grimness of the mountains and the great crying loneliness of the bogs and the wild and impersonal sweep of the ocean around them. They see the supernatural in everything—the flight of birds and the sounds of the wind and the colors of the ocean and the silences of the night. They are a people halfway between this world and some other world and they listen to one with one ear and to the other with a sharper inner ear.

"They're the last people in the world among whom a miracle could occur because they believe in miracles. And talking about miracles, what do you think of the stranger?"

The priest was not prepared to have the conversation veer off of the topic of the Stone of Mananaan in this manner but he had been wanting for some time to discuss the stranger with the doctor and welcomed the chance.

"I don't know anything about him," he said cautiously. "But I hear some strange stories told of him. Of course, strange stories would be told of anyone from outside coming into Killknock. What do you think of him yourself?"

"Well, mind you, I've not met him myself. We are the two people in the village who were the most likely to meet him and get to know him. And it strikes me as odd that neither one nor the other of us has spoken to him, though he is well known to the villagers. It is almost as if whatever brought him to Killknock has to do with them and not with us."

"You think he came here for some special purpose?" asked the priest.

"I know he did," said the doctor. "He announced that he had some business in the village that brought him here—business that he had at one time thought could

take care of itself, but now he found he had to attend
to personally."

"I wonder what he meant by that?" said Father Dimmock half to himself.

"Do you know the thought that crossed my mind
immediately I heard of it? It was that his business had
something to do with someone dying in these parts."

The priest was not as imaginative as the doctor. "You
mean he might be a relative of one of the villagers who
passed on recently?" he asked.

"No," said the doctor. "I mean he might be interested
in someone who hasn't passed on yet, as you so tenderly
put it. He has come here about someone who is to die."

"Well, there's a strange fancy for you," said the
priest.

"Yes," said the doctor. "It is. But that was the thought
that crossed my mind. You know of course that he's a
healer—a sort of miracle worker."

"I'd heard a word passed on the subject," said the
priest cautiously.

"Well, he is. He cured Feeney of deafness. I didn't
believe that at first. I thought it was all just a coincidence.
But I believe he cured him now. And he's made Caitlin
of the Other House young again. I didn't believe that
either but I did after I saw her. No, it wasn't then either,
that I believed it. It was later. She told me that he had
promised her she would have a child of her own."

"Bah," said the priest. "Any tinker will make a barren woman feel young by telling her that."

"Well, he's not a tinker and he made her young and I believe she will have a child of her own," said the doctor, reaching for the whiskey decanter. The priest watched him narrowly and concluded that the whiskey was having its effect upon Doctor McEwan.

"There's another thing he did," said the doctor. "He took little Mairin Rincey up in the air into the great stream of wind that flows over Ireland across the Atlantic to Newfoundland and showed her how the geese migrate along it in their hundreds of thousands so high up they are out of sight of every creature on the face of the earth.

"He also took her to a jungle river in South America. The surface of the river was the color of melted lead and the branches of the trees met over the top of it like the roof of a cathedral.

"There was a little island in the center of the river where it was wider and the sun came down on that like the flashing of a diamond. There were flowers of every kind growing on the island, some as big as plates, and birds colored like jewels came around them and they could understand what the birds were saying. Some were hummingbirds, little flashes of red and green, and some were black as crows but had bright yellow beaks the size of a banana. I expect she meant toucans.

"There was also a black panther and she brought her

three small cubs to them. Mairin wanted one of the cubs
and the panther said that she would be sorry to part with
them, but she might come back any time she wanted and
play with them.

"Well you know how it is with children. Mairin
asked for the loan of the panther kitten and the stranger
promised the panther that it would be returned to her.
She has it up at the house now. It's a darling little thing
with a tongue as rough as a rasp even though it's no
bigger than the corner of a postage stamp."

"Stuff and nonsense," said the priest. "Where did
you get all this anyway?"

"Mairin told me," replied the doctor, looking at him
calmly. "They'll be going back to the jungle island tomorrow to return the kitten. I'm going to see the stranger
myself before they go. Rincey's doomed. There's nothing I can do to help him, and putting him in the hospital
in Galway won't help him either. If there's any man
on earth who can cure him it will be the stranger. I
am going to ask him to cure Rincey—for Mairin."

"And you a doctor?" said the priest astounded.

"And me a doctor," said the other. "Caitlin the Other
House showed me a stone in the road and a mountain
behind it and said that the stone represented everything I
knew and the mountain the things I didn't know but
were true anyway. And she was right.

"There's another odd thing about the stranger," he
went on. "It was the night before he came that the Man

of Stone and the Woman of Stone on the mountain behind the O'Flaherty cottage tipped over on their faces. When I heard about that I checked the Galway papers and the ones I get from England thinking there had been an earthquake somewhere and that had toppled them over. But there was no earthquake. None at all. Anywhere in the world."

"You're taking too much of the whiskey," said the priest, "and I can see I will get no help out of you on the problem of the Stone of Mananaan. Well. It's as I thought. I'll have to tackle the problem myself and I was right the first time. The stone has to be pulled down."

"You know," said the doctor, coddling the whiskey in his glass, swilling it around as was his custom, and ignoring the priest's remark about the amount he was drinking, "I have a feeling that the reason the stranger is in the village has something to do with the Stone of Mananaan. When you came here I didn't think that way. But talking to you about it and about him has given me the feeling. I think you can leave the Stone of Mananaan alone. And whoever put the coppers and the dead fish before it; I think the stranger will attend to it all himself."

"It isn't his business to attend to it," said the priest angrily. "It is my business."

He got up to go but the doctor remained seated,

nursing his whiskey and looking into the warm golden glisten it made in the glass.

"I wouldn't say it isn't his business," he said. "It may be more his business than yours."

But the priest was already out of the door and did not hear him.

Chapter Eleven

THAT night the wind rose a little, coming in erratic and nervous puffs off the ocean, slamming a shutter here and a gate there and causing the dogs to howl and the cattle to stir uneasily in the fields and the sheep, who were reduced in the dark to uncertain blobs of luminosity on the mountain sides, to gather together in little gullies and clefts and ravines and stamp their feet nervously.

Out on the ocean it was quite calm, but the mark of the wind could be seen in scurries of dirty white on the water, and the sky, which had been deep and dark like an eternity of nothingness, was covered with a ghostly rag of cloud.

144

The stars, which in the blackness of the night had burned fiercely and cruelly, were obscured by the cloud which was like the wrappings off a corpse, and the youths of the village, who were accustomed to gather by the harbor wall to talk in the quiet of the night, felt the change that the puffs of wind brought and went off silently to their cottages.

Rincey, when he returned from the doctor, had dinner with Mairin and the stranger, who was very quiet and drawn in on himself, and then excused himself and went to bed. Mairin had with her a little black kitten which she said belonged to a black panther that lived on an island in the Orinoco River and that she must take it back on the morrow.

But Rincey only half-listened to her fancies, for he was worried by the attitude of the doctor during his examination. He half-feared that the doctor would send him to the hospital in Galway and he was at times of a mind to mention his trouble to the stranger.

But since the man was a guest in his house he did not feel that he should burden him with his troubles. So he said nothing of his anxiety but went to his room and to bed immediately after supper.

For a long time he could not get to sleep. He kept thinking about the pain in his side and wondering to himself whether it was really there or not. He had felt some ease after seeing Mrs. Coleman on Inishlacken and was confident that she had straightened out his bones and that he would soon be rid of the cleddin.

But now he was not so sure that she had helped him.

He tried breathing in deeply and holding his breath and seeing if there was any pain. But between being used to the pain, and being anxious to assure himself that it was not really there at all, he could not make up his mind. There was a little pain. That he could not deny. But it was not a very great pain—not the kind of pain that a man who was a man should take seriously at all. There were times when he was a boy when he had had more pain in his chest than he felt now. Or so he tried to assure himself. And then he tried to tell himself that he really had no pain at all, but it was only the memory of the pain that troubled him.

He refused to think about dying.

God would not let such a thing happen, not because he was particularly worthy and should be allowed to live. He knew that this was not so. It was because if he died, there would be no one to look after Mairin. She would be put somewhere among strangers. God would not let that happen to her because Mairin had done no wrong. So he told himself he would be allowed to live until she was a grown woman and had met and married a man and was set up in the world. Then he, Rincey, would die.

To make sure of this, just before he fell asleep, he got out of bed and kneeled beside it and prayed as hard as he could to be allowed to live, not for himself but for Mairin's sake. Sometimes when he was praying he knew that he was just saying words and all sorts of extraneous thoughts that had nothing to do with his prayers came into his head. He would think of nails or hammers, or a pair of shoes or the smell of the drying seaweed in the harbor or a man he had spoken to earlier in the day.

But at other times, when he was praying he felt a direct and immediate communication between him and his Creator, as if they were quite alone in the whole universe and there was no other sound in the whole of space but his own voice talking to God. He felt this way now when he was praying to be allowed to live for Mairin's sake. Then he got back into bed and, much eased in his conscience, he fell asleep.

He did not sleep well though. His dreams were troubled. They were of fleeting and terrible glimpses of things in his past life which had either happened to him or he fancied had happened to him.

At one time he was being taken by his father up a circular staircase to the top of a castle. When he got there, out of the confinement of the staircase which wound round and round in the wall of the castle, his father was gone and he was alone on the battlement with the world far away at his feet. Then the walls of the castle started to fall slowly toward the earth, swinging outward and downward, and he cried out and woke with a start, his heart beating excitedly.

When he went to sleep again he dreamed for a while of a beautiful island. Mairin was on it and she had come to this island with him to return the panther kitten to its mother. She went into a thicket of flowers and he was left alone on the beach. And then the beach changed and it was Copul Beach where the man had been shot during the troubles, running into the ocean for succor.

And then he was face to face with the policeman he had killed in retaliation and the policeman was trying to take off his jacket and swearing that he would have nothing more to do with the police and talking about his wife and his children. And then the gun in Rincey's hand exploded and kicked and there was a blotch of blood on the policeman's forehead and he went down to the ground with a look of pleading and disbelief on his pale fat face, and Rincey cried out in his sleep, "No! No! No!"

Then he woke up again and saw the stranger standing in his room by the side of his bed looking down at him.

"I heard you cry out," said the stranger, "so I came to you."

"I have had a terrible dream," said Rincey. His eyes were still black with the fear of the dream and when he put his hand to his face it was trembling.

"You are a good man, sir," he said. "I know that you

are a good man and I wish that you could cure me of this dream that comes to me many times."

"Tell me about it," said the stranger and he sat on the bed beside him.

"I will indeed, for I think it will ease me. But it is a shame that I should burden you with it and you a guest in my house."

"We are all brothers one to the other from birth to death," said the stranger. "There is no host and guest when anyone is in trouble."

"It is a man that I have killed," said Rincey in a great rush as if he must get the words out very fast or the opportunity for speaking would be gone never to return again. "He was a man who was pleading for his life and talking of his children and I shot him and killed him and from the moment that I did it I would sooner be dead myself. And if my own death would bring him back to life, I would have died gladly a thousand times since then."

Then he told the whole story of the killing and of how at the most unexpected times, sometimes in the middle of the day working at his last, or walking with Mairin or sitting down to a meal, the memory of it would return to him bringing the sharpest agony.

He lay back in bed while he was telling the story with his hands over his chest and clasped as if he were praying and the stranger sat silently on the bed listening to him.

When he had done, the stranger said nothing and the only noise there was was the moaning of the wind over the ocean and the little booming noise it made over the harbor wall and the hiss of it past the eaves of the house. There was a candle in the room and the yellow flame of it would flutter now and again when the wind slammed against the window, and the flickering of the flame rearranged the shadows and the darkness in the place, so that it was as if all the innocent dead in the world were listening to what was being said by the cobbler, and weaving and bowing about the room and the walls.

Rincey had closed his eyes when he was telling his tale, for he did not want to look at the stranger, lest, seeing him there, he might be tempted to justify what he had done or at least mitigate it in some degree. It was important to him that he should plainly set forth, in all its horror, the crime that he had committed; for if he did not do so he would be left with some remnant of it to torture him when the stranger had gone away.

When he had finished he opened his eyes and looking at the stranger saw that the stranger's face was not stern but was filled with such a profound sadness that the sight of it brought a catch to his throat.

The sight so moved Rincey that he cried, "God's pity on you. You have had woes enough and I have only added to them. Forgive me that I have put so much sorrow upon you. I would rather not have been born than have added to your hurts."

He reached and took the stranger's hand in his own which were so enlarged by his years of cobbling. He hoped that by holding the stranger's hand in his he could, in some little degree, abate the deep sorrow that lay so deeply on him.

"You do not know who I am, Rincey the Cobbler?" asked the stranger.

"I know that you are a good man, sir," said Rincey. "Better than any man that was ever in the world."

He was fondling the stranger's hand and felt the scar on the back of it that he had first noticed the day he met the stranger in Feeney's saloon. Suddenly he was filled with wonder and he looked directly into the stranger's face in the soft glow of the candlelight and whispered in awe, "Is it you? Is it you that I have had in my own house and with only my child for company?"

"It is I," said the stranger.

"Forgive me that I did not know you," said Rincey.

"There are many who meet me and do not know me," the stranger replied, "and many who think they know me and do not know me at all.

"I said that I would be with my people until the end of the world, but they have forgotten that I said it. Or they look for me in some shining form forgetting that when I was first among them it was as the son of a carpenter from a village as small as this one. They have forgotten that I was a man and being man may appear among them as one of themselves. But there is this difference that whatever wrong is done in the world, it is I who suffer, and all the wrongs of the world are my continuing sorrow."

"I am troubled about Mairin," said Rincey after a while. "I do not know what will become of her alone in the world."

"She will not be without love," said the stranger, "and you will not be troubled any more by your sin. You were troubled before because you pitied yourself because you had done it. But now you have pitied me and it is forgiven you." When he had said this the stranger left the room and Rincey was filled with a great sense of peace and fell asleep.

The following morning Dr. McEwan, passing early down the village, met the stranger and Mairin going up the street together. The child was carrying a black kitten in her arms and when the doctor stopped the stranger, Mairin went on ahead a few paces, talking to the kitten.

"I wanted to speak to you about Rincey," said the doctor. "I wanted to ask you to help him." He nodded toward Mairin and added, "For the child."

"The help you want for him I cannot give," said the stranger, "because his time has come. But he had a deeper hurt than you know of and that is cured and will trouble him no more."

He smiled and Dr. McEwan said afterwards that it was a teasing kind of smile, as between friends, and he did not know whether the stranger was piquing him in that he, a doctor, had asked for help with a sick man, or whether, as he averred to the priest, it was because he, the doctor, was the only Protestant in the village.

"I am going to take Mairin away with me for a while," the stranger said. "It will be better for her. Then I will bring her back. If people ask where she is, say that she is with me and in good hands. In any case, she has a promise to fulfill."

With that he turned and rejoined Mairin and the doctor stood watching them.

Later that day he called on Rincey and found the cobbler dead of a massive lung hemorrhage. He could not have had much pain, for his hands were crossed peacefully on his chest and his lips, long pursed with the task of holding nails in his mouth, were relaxed in a smile.

Chapter Twelve

THE church of Killknock was perhaps the ugliest building in the village, none of whose structures were distinguished for beauty. Built of limestone blocks, it had a kind of prison look to it, a harsh, cold, forbidding air that was accentuated rather than relieved by the false flying buttresses that supported the grim sides. Many churches in Ireland have this look which is quite the opposite of that of the few pathetic ruins of the early Celtic churches that are full of charm and forgiveness.

The church of Killknock had been built, like the majority of Irish churches, in the middle of the nine-teenth century following that particular Act of Parliament that permitted the Irish to worship in their faith openly and freely. At that time the land was at its poorest, and there were only pennies for building where pounds were needed. A limited budget dictated a stern structure; a large gray stone box with but the smallest windows since glass was expensive. The false flying buttresses had been added in a desperate attempt to get rid of the prison look of the place. But they were a failure.

There was never the money in Killknock to build a new church nor even to decorate the structure that had been erected. The floor was of flagstones, now much worn. The interior walls were plastered and washed down with slaked lime and were badly in need of re-plastering. The benches for the worshipers were of the cheapest deal which had been varnished many many years before with the cheapest varnish.

It had turned in places a repelling yellow and in others was quite worn away so that the bare deal showed. There was a statue of Saint Colman on one side of the altar and of Saint Joseph on the other. In one of the wings, giving off the altar, was a smaller area containing the baptismal font which was of cement poured into a mold to take the shape of an unlovely bowl. On the other wing there was a tomb, also of cement, and on it an incription saying that it contained the remains of Father Michael O'Driscoll who had died in the parish during the Famine. He had died of starvation, for what food came his way he gave to the parishioners.

Down the body of the church there were a few ancient standards or large upright poles, supported on the floor by metal brackets. Each contained a banner of tin plate with on it the *Saint Colman, Pray for Us, Saint Brendan, Pray for Us* and so on. Originally these tin banners had been painted white and the wording had been black and had perhaps looked quite effective. But the white had long faded to a caricature of brown and the black was merely dirty-looking and the whole effect dingy in the extreme.

For this the villagers were not to be blamed. They were poor, their priest was poor and the total collection from the parish hardly exceeded five hundred pounds a year.

That was scarcely enough to keep the church in repair and provide food and clothing for the priest. There was none left for beautification.

The harshness of the church was not relieved by the churchyard around. Here there was a multitude of graves over which the grasses grew rank and long. Some areas had been taken over by thickets of wild rose and others by blackberries. Such headstones as there were were cheap and askew by neglect, for it is not an Irish custom to care for graves and that for the reason that there is nothing in a grave but the mortal remains of the departed. The soul is in another world altogether and to take care of a grave is to suggest that the body is more important than the soul.

Despite its uncompromisingly repellent appearance, the parishioners were fond and proud of their church and would have strongly resisted any move to replace it with another or even to improve it in any great degree. The oldest men in the village could remember entering it as awe-struck boys, with their ears red and tingling from a last-minute scrubbing by their mothers, and their hair stuck down on their heads by water hastily slapped on it a few moments before the Mass bell.

It was the place they came to confess their sins, the place they came to receive a renewal of the grace of God, the place they witnessed, Sunday after Sunday, the awesome miracle of the Mass, the place where they had been married and the place from whence their bodies would be taken to be buried in the untidy churchyard outside. Such a place as that no man wishes changed, nor would he find it any better for being changed even if the grim limestone walls were to be replaced by walls of purest crystal.

God dwelt in the church. You could feel His presence as you came past the door, the thick ugly door with its brown varnish on it. When you came around the corner of that door and caught a glimpse of the altar in the gray light that struggled through the high narrow windows you were in the presence of God. You could feel the holiness and it made you young again.

"I will go to the altar of God," was what the priest said in Latin at the start of the Mass.

And the reply to this, said aloud by the altar boys and to themselves by the congregation was, "To God who gave me the joy of my youth."

The church was always crowded for Sunday Mass, the people coming over in their curraghs from Inishlacken.

Rincey the cobbler had died on Thursday. That morning Mairin had gone away with the stranger and she had returned that afternoon, looking sad and carrying a strange red flower.

By good fortune, Dr. McEwan was at Rincey's house with the women who were laying out the corpse when the girl returned. He took her aside into the kitchen, through all the women in their black shawls who looked at her mutely, too full of grief for her to speak.

He cleared the kitchen of them and made her sit in a chair by the hearth and racked his brains in a panic for some way to tell her that her father was dead—a way that would not be a shock to her.

"Now, my dear," he said eventually, "you have to be a brave little girl. Your father has not been a well man. He was not a well man at all. There was a great deal of pain ahead for him."

"Himself is not here," said Mairin. She always referred to her father as "himself."

"What do you mean by that?" asked the doctor, startled out of his preparations to break the news to her gently.

"Well, I'm not to cry," she said, as if repeating a lesson. "And I'm trying not to cry and if you would stop looking at me that way it would be easier for me." The doctor turned to examine the dishes on the dresser in the kitchen, for he could hear the tears behind her voice.

"Well, it was this way," said Mairin after a pause to get control of herself. "I went with the stranger to give back the kitten to its mother on the island in the middle of the river with the trees all around it except that they were not over the top of the island which was in the sun. And I gave the kitten back and the mother let me play with the other kittens and all the time the stranger was with me and he played with the kittens too.

"Then he said that he had to go away from me soon but all that that meant was that I wouldn't be able to see him. I didn't want him to go away so I could not see him any more and I begged him to take me and do you know what he said to that?"

"No," said the doctor, "I don't."

"He said the only way I could be with him and go flying with the wild geese again and to the island that we were on and to the ice palaces that are up in the northern part of the world beyond where the geese go and to other places that he took me was by dying, and he did not want me to die yet because he had something he wanted me to do."

She stopped talking for a while, and hunched up in the chair with the red flower in her hand, she twisted it around in her fingers, examining it very closely all the while. Then she gave the doctor a look that was one of cunning and innocence at the same time.

"I'll tell you what I did," she said. "I made a bargain with him." Then she added, "It wasn't exactly a bargain but it was an arrangement, for a girl would be very foolish indeed if she accepted everything that was put before her and didn't use her own mind to get something a little better that wouldn't hurt anybody at all."

"What did you do?" asked the doctor.

"I don't know that I should be letting you in on the secret," said Mairin, "but I'll tell you anyway. Whenever I asked Himself, that is Mr. Rincey, for a penny for an ice cream he would tell me that he had not a penny to spare. But if I asked him if he loved me and then asked him for a penny for ice cream, I always got the penny.

"So I asked the stranger if he loved me and he said he did indeed, and indeed I know it was true. Then I asked him if when I had done what he wanted me to do, he would come and see me again once in a while and take me up with the geese and the swans and to other places, and he laughed for he saw that I had caught him and he said that he would indeed.

"After that we went swimming. There was a lake on the island and the whole surface of it was covered with flowers so that you couldn't see the water for them. Then petals were as smooth as the wax of a candle and some of them were pink like the palm of your hand and some of them were white and some of them were gold like the gold a buttercup makes when you put it under your chin. You've done that, I suppose?"

"I have," said the doctor. "When I was a boy."

"Well, that was the color they were. Not really gold but softer. It was the loveliest thing you ever saw and we swam around among the flowers and when you raised your hand out of the water it was like dripping diamonds onto the petals of them. When we got out on the other side Himself was there waiting for us and I knew he had died."

She fell silent for a while and then said in a very small voice, "If I tell you anything more I'll cry and they told me not to cry but to think of the lake with the flowers and the island where everybody was happy."

But it was Dr. McEwan who was weeping. He picked her up out of the chair and held her in his arms very tightly and said, "You're to stay with me. I'll take you home this very night."

Then he put her down and his Scots practicality getting the better of his sentiment, he blew his nose and said, "Is there anything you will want to take from the house?"

"No," said Mairin. "There's nothing I want from the house but they let me take this flower back with me from the island."

He took it from her and looked at it closely. He recognized it as a tropical flower—a hibiscus. And he wasn't in the least surprised.

The funeral service was held the following day in the prisonlike church that Rincey had attended since his boyhood and the body was buried in the wild rank churchyard outside. At the conclusion of the funeral service and before the coffin was taken outside for burial, Father Dimmock said that he wanted all the men to come back into the church after the interment.

When the burial was over, the men came back into the church and the priest addressed them from the altar steps. "There is something we have to get rid of in this parish," he said. "Something that is a symbol of the superstition and lack of godliness among the people. It is an evil thing that has remained from the old pagan times of Ireland and it is time that it was removed.

"I mean that stone on top of the mountain," he continued, gesturing toward it. "There are people in this parish who pretend to be Christians and Catholics and are still paying tribute to that stone which is nothing but a pagan idol.

"Dr. McEwan was up there the other day and he

found some copper pennies put before that stone and the remains of a little fish and that was done by someone in this parish. They may tell themselves that they only did it for good luck and that there is no harm in it. But there is great harm in it, for that is nothing else but idolatry disguised as an innocent gesture.

"Let the man who put those things in front of that stone examine the state of his soul in the eyes of God. He is in mortal danger. But there are many others who are in a similar danger, for they pay a kind of reverence to that stone on the mountain top. They will not approach it without first getting a piece of heather and a blade of sally grass and a round pebble. That again is a disguised idolatry. It is a secret worship of the old pagan god Mananaan. There must be an end to these idolatrous superstitions and I have selected the time for the end to come.

"Tomorrow night every man in this church will come with me, with a pick or a shovel or some such implement, and we will go together to the mountain top and dig up that most wicked of the stones—the Stone of Mananaan. We will topple it down and break it up and that will be an end to this evil business."

When the priest had said these words there was a little shiver among the men in the church.

"You will meet me here tomorrow evening after Benediction," the priest said. "And you will have your tools with you. I will lead you up the mountain."

Then he made a gesture of dismissal and the men went out of the church silently past the freshly covered grave of Rincey. None of them dared turn to look up at the peak of the mountain behind them with the Stone of Mananaan standing on it darkly against the night sky.

Chapter Thirteen

WHEN they had left the church following the instruction of the priest, the men collected in Feeney's bar, for the day had been full of emotional stress for them and they had a need to talk it over together over a glass of Guinness. The death of Rincey the cobbler had saddened them all and if that had been the only event of the day, it would have been well sufficient to justify a gathering at Feeney's. The old custom of the wake had been banished from the village by Father Dimmock in that war against paganism that he had commenced when he first came to the parish as its shepherd.

Father Dimmock did not understand or pretended not to understand the reason for the custom of the wake. A wake was actually a final act of charity toward the deceased. In other countries it was and is the custom to send wreaths of flowers to put on the grave as a mark of the esteem in which the dead was held by his friends. The more flowers and the more expensive the flowers, the greater had been his circle of friends upon earth.

But the Irish have little use for such secondhand tribute. The wake then was a gathering not of flowers but of the dead man's friends. The more of them, the greater the tribute to his memory. The more pipes of tobacco that were smoked and the more nips of whiskey and glasses of Guinness consumed, then the greater the tribute to the affection in which he had been held. And all this was done, of course, not with the dead man cold in his grave and six foot of wet clay cutting him off from his friends, but with his corpse lying there in the house, with the smell of the whiskey and the tobacco and the Guinness about him for comfort.

It was the custom at a wake to tell stories of the man's life—not whispered little sobs of what a good kind of man he had been and how much he would be missed, but loudly told, rowdy stories of the scrapes that he had been in and out of in his life, until the men at the wake were rolling with laughter at the bright memories and the spirit of the dead man comforted by

the pleasure he had given to all and the esteem in which
he had been held.

But Father Dimmock was dead set against wakes and
insisted that the body be brought to the church and
remain there twenty-four hours before burial. And you
could hardly take the body out of the church back to
his own house to hold a wake. And so the wake went.

But the men met in Feeney's bar anyway, feeling
badly that there had been no wake for Rincey, and
determined to talk over the episodes of his life and have
a laugh about it. Feeney had laid in a stock of clay pipes
that they would smoke. And when they were through,
he would collect the clay pipes and put them on Rincey's
grave so that Rincey would know how many of the
men of the village had had a drink and a smoke to his
memory and this would be a comfort to him.

But they had more to talk about than Rincey when
they collected in the bar. They had to talk about the
terrible task the priest had sent them—the task of throwing over the Stone of Mananaan on the top of the
mountain.

"The old stone has been up there for two thousand
years and more," said one, when he had got and paid for
his glass of Guinness. "What sense is there to throwing
it down now? Is there any man here that can show me
the sense of it?" And he took a judicious sip of the Guinness and put it carefully down on the little shelf that ran
around the wall of the room.

"Well, the priest said that it was an occasion of super-stition and idolatry," said another. "And superstition and idolatry are clean forbidden by the Church as you all well know."

"And how has it become all of a sudden an occasion of superstition?" demanded the first man. "Will you answer me that now? Hasn't it been there all these years —two thousand years or maybe three thousand years— and it's only in the last five minutes so to speak that the priest has discovered that it is sinful.

"Does he think now that he is a better man than the priests we had before him? Haven't all the priests that have ever been in this parish had the good sense to let the old stone alone? And if they left it alone why doesn't he have the sense to leave it alone and not go troubling things that he doesn't know anything about?"

"I'll tell you what it is," said Tim Conneeley with great deliberation from the corner by the fire. "I'll tell you what it is. It's all that new learning that they are giving to the priests these days. There was a time when all they had to do was to hear the call of God to become a priest. But now the call of God isn't good enough. They have to have a diploma as well. Do you suppose now that when Christ said to Peter to follow Him He first of all inquired whether he had a diploma from Maynooth?"

"And I'll tell you something else," said another. "If there was any harm in the old stone at all, wouldn't Saint

Patrick have sent it out of the land over to England the same as he did with the snakes and them other stones they have somewhere in England?"

"You'll be meaning Stonehenge," said Feeney who had been to England.

"The same. The stone was here when Patrick was here and if he had found any harm in it at all he would have sent it to England or thrown it into the sea. And if it was a decent stone for the Blessed Saint himself, I don't see why Father Dimmock should quarrel with it."

"Well, you see," said Feeney, "it's the pennies that were put in front of it, and the fish. They're a kind of a tribute to the stone and that's what stuck in his throat. Mind you," he continued, "I don't think he'd have been so wild about it at all if it wasn't Dr. McEwan who had found them there, and him a Protestant, and from the Six Counties, God help him."

"And what's the harm with putting down a few pennies in front of a stone for good luck?" demanded Tim Conneeley. "There's wells all over the world that are chock-full of pennies that people have thrown into them for luck. And doesn't every American that comes to Ireland kiss the stone in Blarney Castle, and the man who holds them from falling down and breaking their skulls the brother of a priest so I've heard.

"Now tell me, is he going to throw over Blarney Castle next and cover up every well in Ireland that people throw a coin into?"

"I'll tell you what it is," said Feeney, who delighted to take part in a conversation now that he could hear. "These things are older than Father Dimmock thinks and there is no harm in them at all, at all. If you threw down every stone in Ireland there'd be a new set of lucky or unlucky stones around the country one minute later, for there's a kind of a need on people to have these things. I don't know what kind of a need it is, but it's there all right. I remember a man came into this bar once that had a grouse foot on the end of his watch chain for luck. He was a Presbyterian," he added.

So the talk went on. The more the problem was examined the more the men of Killknock could see no reason why the Stone of Mananaan, which had stood so long on the mountain top above the village, overlooking everything in it including the church, should be toppled to the ground.

But if they were honest with themselves they would have admitted that it was not reason alone that brought them to this conclusion, but fear. They were afraid of tampering with the stone that their fathers and their grandfathers and their ancestors for twenty and more generations had held in awe. They had learned to hold it in awe from their parents who had learned it from their parents and so on for uncounted generations. And there was a direct blood link between them, for all the modernity of the world around, with the people who had first erected the stone and carved the facelike circle at the top of it. Perhaps it was in the indestructible genes, passed from one generation to another, that the awe concerning the stone lay. But it was there. To throw it down would bring some kind of disaster. To attempt to throw it down was an appalling folly, not to be contemplated seriously.

So, inevitably the discussion turned to some plan for preventing the priest's carrying out his purpose. But here they were up against the character of Father Dimmock and they well knew that he was such a man that he would not be shaken from his purpose by any petition on their part. Indeed, he would condemn them for approaching him on the subject and see in their action a confirmation of the great spiritual need for throwing the stone over once and for all.

Tim Conneeley suggested the solution. "It will take a lot of men working with a lot of tools to put the stone down," he said in his slow judicial way. "A lot of men. And a lot of tools. It's the greatest pity that the only pick I have to me name I broke the handle while working on the roads a month ago."

"There was a good spade I had," said another. "You would not find a better spade in the whole of Connemara. It had a good point on the end of it for working around rocks. You know how it is that some spades are not clever around rocks and others have the feel of the thing and go willingly to the task. And that spade is lost entirely."

I haven't set eyes upon it in three months and I think it was stolen by one of those men in Inishlacken."

"A crowbar would be a useful thing for working on the stone," said Feeney. "There was a good crowbar here at one time. I remember I used it to open the old safe in the back that the lock got stuck on. But from that day to this I haven't set eyes on it, and that was four years ago."

And so it went. In half an hour's conversation the village was bereft of tools and the matter having been settled in this way the men turned to talk of Rincey and the great fellow he had been in his time. And the talk went so merrily and heartily that when the sergeant came to close the bar, he hadn't the heart to do it. But he remembered his duty. The law said that the bar was to be closed at ten o'clock and thereafter drinks were to be served only to bona fide travelers, on their way from one place to another.

When he came in and saw the men standing around with their Guinness and knew that they were waking Rincey, he scratched his head for a moment and looking at nobody in particular he said, "I suppose that every man jack in this room is a traveler and entitled under the laws of the Republic to take a drop after hours."

"That's a true word you spoke there," said Tim Conneeley. "A true word indeed and none truer. For every man among us is traveling from the cradle to the grave and a greater journey there is not to be seen on the face of the earth."

"Close the doors then," said the sergeant, "and let us have a drink together to help us on the way."

Tom Joyce did not join the group in Feeney's bar that night. He was at the funeral service and the burial and he was in the church when the priest made his pronouncement about the stone. But he went immediately to his own house which was but a few doors from the church and there he sat with a great fear on him that the stone was to be overturned.

He did not know what to do to prevent it. So, in desperation, he alone of the villagers went to the priest to attempt to get him to change his mind.

"What is it you want?" asked Father Dimmock when Tom Joyce had been admitted to his study by the housekeeper.

"It is about the stone," said Tom. "You cannot throw it down."

"And why not?" demanded the priest.

"Because it is a thing belonging to the village from olden times and you have no right to interfere with it."

"It is an unclean relic of heathen times that exercises an evil influence on the minds of the people of my flock and for that reason it is to go," snapped the priest.

"I will tell you something you do not know," said the fisherman. "The stranger will not let you throw down the stone. If you attempt it, there will be a lot of sorrow in this village."

"The stranger?" said the priest, startled.

"The same," said Tom Joyce. "I was up on the mountain top once and when I got near to it I saw him standing there. And when I got nearer still the stranger had turned into the stone. I saw it myself."

"You're a fool," said the priest. "An ignorant fool, and it is this kind of nonsense that had made me decide on doing away with the stone once and for all."

"The stranger is not in the village now, is he?" asked the other.

"No."

"You do not know where he is?"

"No."

"I know where he is. I could find him for you."

"And where is he?" demanded Father Dimmock.

"If you were to go up to the top of the mountain before the Stone of Mananaan, and if you were to call to the stranger standing before the stone, he would step out of it to you."

"You are talking nonsense," roared the priest. "You are either drunk or out of your mind."

"I am neither drunk nor out of my senses," replied Tom Joyce. "There are things in Ireland that were here before Patrick and they are still here. And all the people know that though they will not tell you so to your face.

"I do not have to tell you who the stranger is. You

know it for yourself. He is the one after whom the mountain was named in its old name. And he was the one who saved me in the White Storm when you had all left the village and I was out in the ocean in my curragh. And if you touch that stone you will bring ruin on the village and on yourself."

"Sober you are a Christian and drunk you are a heathen, Tom Joyce," said the priest, "and that is the way with drink and the Irish. Go home now and sleep off the Guinness and meet me here tomorrow and you will be ashamed of everything you have said tonight."

Tom Joyce rose and went to the door. "I've warned you," he said. "There was a reason that stone has stood there through thousands of years. Think of that before you set out to tear it down." And with that he left.

He did not however go to his bed, but to the little shed in the back yard of his house where he kept a few tools. He took a pick and a shovel which he put in the bottom of a sack. Then he slung the sack over his back and started to climb directly from his back yard up the flank of the mountain toward the summit.

The moon had not yet risen. He climbed slowly and purposefully, full of fear but determined on what he was going to do. When he reached the peak of the mountain and stood before the Stone of Mananaan, he looked at the stone and it seemed to be moving up and over him as the clouds glided by over his head in the black vault of the sky. When he first looked up in this manner he knew that it was the clouds that were moving and the stone that was standing still. But after a little while it came to him that it was the clouds that were still, frozen against their backdrop of infinity, and the stone that was soaring toward and above him with tremendous speed and power and silence. He was filled with awe by this silent movement of the stone and the thought that it had been moving like this, and yet remaining in the same place, for thousands of years and he alone realized it. In the old times before Patrick, people had known that this was the movement of the stone, but he was the only one since then who knew of it. The link between him and the pre-Christians and between him and the stone seemed in that moment strong and intimate and unbreakable.

He did not say anything, for there were no words he could utter that would express his sense of wonder. After a little while he turned from watching the spectacular leap of the stone against the heavens and looked out toward the ocean which the stone faced and had watched through thirty centuries.

The ocean was dark except for one silver streak toward the horizon. The darkness of the ocean came into the shore and mingled with it, so that it was impossible to tell where shore and ocean met—where one ended and the other began. They were one—the land and the water—and standing there on the mountain he could feel in his feet and legs the movement of the sea as he had felt it many times in his curragh. This strong strange mountain of rock was responding to the gentle and eternal undulation of the waves of the ocean and had done so through all time and he was the only man who could feel it. It comforted him to sense the movement of the sea on the mountain and it comforted him too that far out on the horizon there was that one serene streak of light, lying like hope upon the dark waters of the world.

Below, at the foot of the mountain, were a few more little points of puny light which he knew were the lights in the houses of the village. The sight of them filled him with contempt and anger. These lights were the work of men who did not understand the ocean and the mountain and the Stone of Mananaan. They lived close to a great mystery and they did not know about it, but in their impertinence they would throw the stone down and violate beliefs far more ancient than those they held now.

Presently he remembered what he had come to the mountain top to do and reaching into his sack, took out the pick and started to dig, keeping his face toward the stone all the time. The pick bit readily into the limestone at the base of the stone and he had soon enough of it worked loose to get his shovel and move it away and then fall to with the pick again. While he was working he did not look up at the stone at all. But he could picture it streaming over him against the night sky and he began to be afraid of it.

"I am doing what I must do," he said aloud at one time. "It is not my will to do it, but it must be done. Do not harm me then, for I am your man and you and I know each other." And he went on digging until he had produced a deep pit at the base of the stone and his spade reached something soft in the rock. At that he flung the spade aside, and lying on the ground reached downward with his hands. But his reach was not long enough and so he thrust his shoulders down into the pit with his head and arm completely inside of it. For a second he thought that he had not made the hole wide enough and so the sides were pressing on his broad shoulders. And then, struggling a little more, he touched what lay in the bottom of the hole. And suddenly he screamed.

Below, in Feeney's bar, the men continued telling their stories about Rincey and drinking the Guinness. Suddenly Feeney held up his hand.

"Did you hear that?" he asked.

"What was it?" demanded Tim Conneeley.

"I heard a shriek," said Feeney. "And it came from the top of the mountain."

"What kind of a shriek was it?" asked th sergeant.

"It was like the cry of a soul as it plunges into the pit of Hell," said Feeney and he crossed himself.

Chapter Fourteen

THE bishop was a very old man and his flesh had about it the look of a rubber balloon which has been partially filled not with air but with water. In places it bulged heavily and sullenly and in others it sank equally heavily and sullenly. His eyes were rimmed with red around the lids, as if they must be extremely painful, open or shut, and the few white hairs upon his head had a coarse look to them as if they had long been dead but had neglected to fall out and remained now like a few strands of white kelp attached to his scalp. His hands were small but swollen with his years and he was compelled to wear shoes with elastic insets, for his feet were swollen also.

He was, for all his appearance, a man who was very old in God. He had given sixty-three years of his life to the service of God and that service had taken him to many strange parts of the world before he was elevated to the episcopal seat in western Ireland.

He had gone through the fire of the younger days of priesthood when the man in him had tortured so terribly the God in him; through all the struggles of the spirit against the flesh, the appalling moments of doubt, of intense temptation when he had wondered whether, young and vigorous, he had not turned his back foolishly upon the delights of the world, the attractions of women with their cool arms and inviting lips, the far and glittering places of yachts and romance and walks in the scented night with a beloved, the allure of fame and wealth and the shouting cheerful challenging noise of the world.

He had gone through all that. The countess in Rome he had met as a young theological student, and who was as lovely as a willow with the promise of spring on it. The girl he had seen in his youth standing beside a wall with the sea wind ruffling her hair and her face all innocence and laughter, and the children he had held in his arms at baptisms with an ache at the knowledge that he could never father a child of his own.

The laity thought that a man had a vocation to the priesthood and thereafter the world had no temptations for him. They forgot that the vocation was to the spirit but the man was of flesh and blood and the demands of flesh and blood were cruelly strong and cruelly unexpected. Then came like a hot and overpowering wind against which his only defense had been to cry out within himself, "Lord save me, or I perish . . ."

And so he had come through the fire, turning constantly to God, following the gentle Christ who as Man had experienced the same temptations and desires. And now he had not many steps more to go along the road. The end was very very near. The flesh was conquered and sloughed around him in his old age, disfiguring his appearance. But his spirit was polished bright with love and service to God and soon his Master would call him out of the world and he would leap joyously into death to greet Him face to face.

The bishop sat now in his chair in his study and listened to the strong and purposeful voice of the strong and purposeful priest who sat before him.

"I found him, Your Grace," he said, "crushed between the stone that is called the Stone of Mananaan and the sacrificial stone before it. He was dead. He had dug a pit between the sacrificial stone and the upright stone, if Your Grace follows me, and his head was down in this pit and his shoulders too. The upright stone had tipped forward and trapped him. He was a sight to chill a . . . to chill a . . ."

"A priest?" suggested the bishop.

"He was indeed, Your Grace. His chest was crushed

and his head was a mass of blood and there wasn't a spark of life in him.

"But there was more than that, Your Grace. When I got enough of the villagers together to get the Stone of Mananaan pushed back and propped upright—and a terrible job they had of it with the rain lashing down and the wind howling around the place, and the body lying there before them—when I got enough of them to get the body out, you wouldn't believe what we found below in the pit."

The bishop closed his red-rimmed eyes very slowly, as if he were afraid of hurting the lids, and then opened them again with the same caution.

"And what did you find?" he asked.

"Well, in the bottom of the pit he had dug there was the body of a boy—and none other than the boy that had been out in the White Storm with Tom Joyce and everybody thought had been lost in the storm."

"That was ten years ago," said the bishop. "It was not decomposed?"

"It was not decomposed at all, Your Grace. And Dr. McEwan—he's from the Six Counties and a Protestant but a very good medical man for all that—said that it was because of the limestone or something in the soil thereabouts.

"It's plain what had happened. Joyce had buried the boy there as an offering to the idol for his own life being saved. And when he knew that I was determined to uproot the stone, he knew it would be found and the fact that he had murdered the lad—for he must have murdered him to my way of thinking—would be found out. So he came to dig it up.

"And the stone fell on him when he reached down to get it and killed him there."

"All this would seem to be primarily a matter for the police," said the bishop.

"But it's the spiritual side that concerns me, Your Grace, and should concern yourself, if you don't mind my making so bold as to say so. For it is a case of sheer idolatry on the part of Joyce, and the villagers are saying that it was the stone that killed him, which is another case of superstition and idolatry, for it attributes a superhuman or divine power to the stone."

The bishop was silent for a while. He knew what he wanted to say but he wanted to be sure to get the right words, so that this strong and vehement priest before him, to whom everything was either black or white, right or wrong, would understand.

"It was of course the Stone of Mananaan that killed him," he said at length.

"But, Your Grace," said Father Dimmock in an urgent whisper, fearful that the rumors about the bishop to the effect that he was not quite right in his mind were true, "we cannot attribute a superhuman power or intelligence —the ability to kill of its own accord—to a pagan block of stone."

"You are three years ordained, is that right?" asked the bishop.

"Four, Your Grace."

"Four. A very short time in which to become acquainted with the ways of God. Has it ever occurred to you, Father, that God may use as His instruments not merely human beings but also inanimate objects if that suits His purpose?

"You young priests, trained in what is called a more scientific age, are often the first to put aside the manifestations of God through inanimate objects. You would limit His powers to living creatures and indeed not merely to living creatures but to human beings. I am not sure that this is not a lack of faith. Man may not, by the use of his will, be able to move a stone. But God can. There are many clearly and fully substantiated miracles that attest to this though perhaps you are not familiar with them.

"The Church has suffered greatly in recent times by the limiting of miracles to those in the realms of medicine. Mere cures in short. But I assure you that if God so willed it He could take the whole of Ireland and put it down in the middle of Tibet."

"Yes, Your Grace," said Father Dimmock.

"That being so, why should you doubt for one moment that God caused this stone to move and crush the man to death—this man who was guilty not only of murder but also of idolatry. What more fitting than that, as an example to others, he should have this man killed by the very idol he venerated?"

"I had not thought of that, Your Grace."

"No," said the bishop, "you had not thought of it."

"Dr. McEwan, Your Grace," said the priest, "says that the stone fell because its foundation or support had been weakened in the first place when Joyce dug the grave for the victim, and that it had been tipping over a little off center against the earth that had been put into the grave. And when this was dug out it tipped over completely and so crushed Joyce."

"I think you told me that Dr. McEwan is a Protestant and from the Six Counties and so he will have to satisfy himself with that kind of explanation. Miracles are forbidden him, poor man, and he is cut off by scientific training from the wonders of God on earth and in the heavens."

"Yes, Your Grace."

Father Dimmock hesitated. He had been going to ask the bishop for permission to say a Mass on the mountain top so as to consecrate it for all time to God and rid it of its superstitious hold on the villagers. But he was not sure that he should do so now.

Still he was a man who, having set out on a course of action, could by no means desist and so he blurted out, "I had been hoping, Your Grace, that you would give me permission to celebrate Mass on the mountain top—to consecrate that place and take away forever the last lingering vestiges of paganism with which it is associated."

"Father," said the bishop slowly, "Mass should be celebrated devoutly in the hearts of men. It is there that God is worshiped and not in particular places. And if you were to celebrate a hundred masses on the top of the mountain you would do nothing to change the minds of those men who attend without deeply participating in the Mass themselves. Attend to the people of your parish, not to the stones standing around on the mountain top, and you will be doing your work."

"I had thought of having the stone thrown down," said the priest.

"Throw the stones down inside the people and not on the mountain tops," said the bishop. "In that way you will do real service to God And have no trouble with lay archaeologists and antiquarians."

The priest was humbled by the admonition of the bishop and reflected that what he was being told was true. There was perhaps too much of a tendency not merely in Ireland but all over the world to think of places as being either blessed or cursed when the Lord was not concerned with places at all, but with people; and it was with the hearts and souls of men rather than with monuments that he was called to work.

Still there was one further aspect of the matter on his conscience and since he was a determined man and not a subtle one, he decided to tell the bishop about it even though it might mean a further reprimand for failure in his duty.

"The night that Joyce was killed, Your Grace," he said, "he came to me and warned me not to throw the stone of Mananaan over as I intended to with the help of the villagers. He said there was a reason that the stone had remained standing there for thousands of years; that it was the spirit of the stone that had saved both himself and the village during the White Storm. And he said that the stranger who was in the village was the spirit of the stone—the god Mananaan."

"What stranger?" asked the bishop.

Father Dimmock realized that he had not mentioned the stranger to the bishop before. So he recounted what he knew of the man; how he was supposed to have cured Feeney of his deafness and made Caitlin the Other House young and promised her a child and had lived in the house of Rincey the cobbler and been the constant companion of Mairin, Rincey's daughter, and filled her head with wild imaginings.

"But to tell you the truth, Your Grace," he concluded, "I never met him. I didn't call on him and he did not call on me. I presumed he was not a Catholic. There was some story that he had business in the village, but I never found out what it was. And he went away the day that Rincey died."

To the priest's annoyance, the bishop was very interested in the stranger.

"The little girl, Mairin, who you say was with this stranger frequently," said the bishop. "Have you brought her with you?"

"Yes," said the priest. "I brought her to put her in the convent and I thought you might like to have a word with her first."

"Bring her in," said the bishop and Mairin, who had been waiting in the anteroom, was brought to him.

"Tell me what you know about the stranger," said the bishop. "But wait a minute first." He fumbled with the drawer of his desk and took out of it a crumpled brown paper bag.

"Do you like bull's-eyes?" he asked, peering into the bag.

"Yes indeed," said Mairin, "but I like liquorice better. The stranger said that you probably wouldn't have any liquorice though."

"And right he was," said the bishop. "I gave the last bit of it away only an hour ago. Now I wonder how he could have known that," he added, looking at the priest.

"He knows everything." said Mairin, taking the bull's-eye and putting it prettily in her mouth. "I found that out the day he saved me from drowning."

"Saved you from drowning?" cried Father Dimmock. "What kind of a story is this?"

"It was the day that we met," said Mairin. "He took me down to Copul Beach and I went out on the rocks and got cut off by the tide and the sea went over me and I was going to be drowned. And then he walked out over the water and picked me up and brought me safely back to the shore."

"Did you see him walk on the sea?" asked the bishop.

"No. Not exactly. But that's what he did. Because his clothes weren't wet nor the ends of his trousers. But his feet were wet, for he had taken off his shoes and socks. So when I knew he had walked out over the water to me I knew who he was. Though nobody else did."

"Did he say who he was?" asked the priest severely.

"He did not," said Mairin. "And there was no need to. But I told him I knew who he was and he said not to tell anybody else, for he wanted them to find out for themselves."

The bishop and priest exchanged glances. "What else did he do?" the bishop asked gently.

"I wanted to know where the wild geese went," said Mairin, " so he took me up in the air with them and we went thousands of miles on a river of wind across the ocean to another land where there were a lot of lakes with forests between. It was wonderful being so high up in the sky with the big geese around me so close I could stroke their necks as they flew beside me. And then another time he took me to a place far far away in the north where there was nothing but ice. But it was the most beautiful place I have ever seen, for the ice had caves in it and was like a palace inside, all green and blue and in places dazzling like diamonds.

"And then he took me to an island in a river of green, and we swam in a lake together. The lake was full of water lilies. And I met a black panther and brought home one of her kittens but I had to take it back. He said I was to bring a flower from the island and show it to you."

"And why did he do that?" said the bishop.

"So that you would believe me," replied Mairin. She had a paper sack with her and she opened it and took out of it the red flower and gave it to the bishop.

"What did he look like?" asked the bishop, almost in a whisper.

"He was the loveliest man I have ever seen," said the girl.

"Were there any marks on him at all?" asked the bishop.

"There were," said Mairin. "He had a big scar on each hand."

"What kind of a scar?"

"It was a scar like someone had driven a spike through them," said the girl.

"And his feet?"

"There were the same scars on his feet."

"How did you know?" asked Father Dimmock, almost angrily.

"Sure I saw them when he was putting on his socks after he had walked over the water to save me from drowning. And I saw them again when we went swimming in the lake together."

"Your Grace," said Father Dimmock, but the bishop silenced him with a gesture of his small, swollen hand.

"My dear," he said to Mairin, "if I told you that it wasn't necessary to bring the flower, would you believe me?"

"Yes," said Mairin. "I believe you now. He said it wouldn't be necessary to bring the flower. But I didn't think you would believe me. Nobody else would have believed me. But he said you would."

The bishop got up laboriously from his chair and walked to the huge window of his study. The drapes of heavy velvet had been pulled over it but he put them aside and looked out into the twilight. His study was on the third floor of the building and he could see over the roofs of the houses to the sky which was a transparent and soft green where the last rays of the sun lay to the west. Beyond the roofs of the houses was the water of the bay— a faded gray in the gathering gloom. On the surface of the quiet water he could see two white swans floating gracefully.

"I never wondered much about geese," he said. "But the swans. They were always the ones for me."

He turned to Mairin and said, "Do you suppose . . . ?"

"Yes," said Mairin. "He said he knew you loved the swans and you would not have long to wait now."

"Thanks be to God," said the bishop.

Still standing at the window and looking at the dying lonely loveliness of the day, he said, "Do not put this child in the convent, Father. Take her to Caitlin the Other House and tell her that this is the child of her own that the stranger promised her."

The girl smiled. "That is what he said I had to do," she said. "I had to be the child of Caitlin the Other House and he would visit me again."

Some weeks later Father Dimmock went to the cottage of Caitlin the Other House to inquire about Mairin and found Caitlin leaning against the wall of her little yard. The sky was gray and the clouds were very high up and etched against them like a black line was a long flock of geese winging northward.

"Is Mairin home?" the priest asked.

For answer the woman looked upward at the flock of geese which swooped down low over the cottage and then soared upward again and headed to the north in the great river of the wind.

The two of them watched the geese flying northward against the gray sky until they were lost in the mists over the mountains to the north and the priest went home, wondering.